Steaming to Kingstown

AND

Sucking Up to Dalkey

First published in 2015

Londubh Books
18 Casimir Avenue, Harold's Cross, Dublin 6w
www.londubh.ie

1 3 5 4 2

Origination by David Parfrey; cover by bluett
Printed by Gráficas Castuera, Navarra, Spain

A Note on the Text
The text is set in Adobe Caslon Pro.
Notices are set in Baskerville.

ISBN: 978-907535-77-2

This book is published with the financial assistance of
the Trinity College Dublin Association and Trust.

STEAMING TO KINGSTOWN

AND

SUCKING UP TO DALKEY

The Story *of*
THE DUBLIN AND KINGSTOWN RAILWAY

GARRETT LYONS

LONDUBH

For Martha, Gareth and Jonathan, who make things worthwhile

{ and }

In memory of 'Fitz', in whose good company I often travelled this line.

Contents

Acknowledgements   7

Foreword by Dr Patrick Prendergast   9

Introduction   11

Illustrations and Maps   13

1   Why the Dublin and Kingstown Railway?   17

2   The Dublin and Kingstown Railway   25

3   The Permanent Way and Its Stations   35

4   The Rails   67

5   The Early Locomotives and Rolling Stock   79

6   Atmospheric to Dalkey   89

7   Later Years   121

Bibliography   133

Other Sources   135

APPENDICES

I   Description of the line of railroad from Dublin to Kingstown,

        adapted from the *Dublin Penny Journal*, 1834   136

II   Taken from *The Repertory of Patent Inventions*

        No. XXI, July 1836   148

III   Extract from Parliamentary Papers, 1846   151

IV   A copy of the flyleaf of the diary of Charles Vignoles for 1833   154

Index   156

Acknowledgements

_____

My profound thanks go to Dr Patrick Prendergast, Provost, Trinity College Dublin, for his support, for writing the foreword for this book and for hosting its launch; to the Trinity Association and Trust for financial support and to Dr Garrett O'Donnell, also of TCD, without whose help and insistence this book would never have seen the light of day.

Warmest thanks to my publisher, Jo O'Donoghue, for her patient and cheerful guidance and to David Parfrey, also of Londubh Books, for his skilled production of this work. Thanks to Syd Bluett for his attractive cover design.

My thanks go to Dr R.C. Cox, TCD, for access to the Grierson Papers, for helpful advice and for expert proofreading and to Dr Dan McCarthy for sight of his work on the Dalkey Tramway.

A special note of thanks to the Reverend Dr Norman Gamble (Honorary Archivist, Irish Railway Record Society) for his help on matters relating to the Dalkey Atmospheric Railway and to him and the IRRS for permission to use images from K.A. Murray's book on the Kingstown Railway. Thanks also to Debra Wenlock for generously allowing us to reproduce her picture, 'The Locomotive *Princess*'.

I am grateful to the following for permission to use images: Sophia Brothers and *Science and Society*, National Railway Museum UK; Luci

Gosling and *The Illustrated London News*; Engineers Ireland; the National Library of Ireland; Aaron Binchy and the Royal Society of Antiquaries of Ireland; and Mike Smith for his image of a Pandrol clip.

Thanks to James Scannell for his help on aspects of the Dalkey Atmospheric Line and to the Ulster Transport Museum for useful information.

I have consulted the works of many authors in putting together this short tale and to them, living and dead, I offer my gratitude.

Garrett Lyons
July 2015

FOREWORD

DR PATRICK J. PRENDERGAST,
PROVOST, TRINITY COLLEGE DUBLIN

F eats of engineering should impress us all. They combine technical skill and scientific expertise with managerial ability and business acumen. The construction of one of the world's first urban railways on the south Dublin coast was such a feat.

The story begins in 1815. The proponents of the railway faced many challenges, both engineering and financial: among them were the building of embankments across the marshland in Booterstown, acquiring land through the estates of the Blackrock gentry and deciding where to open stations to maximise demand – some stations opened then have long since disappeared. It also proved challenging to maintain passenger numbers on the Dún Laoghaire to Dalkey line – the section that ran along what is now 'the Metals', with suction pulling the carriages to Dalkey and gravity allowing them to roll back.

Reading this book will make you, as the author puts it, 'marvel that a small group had the foresight and courage to pioneer so many innovations'. These individuals responded to an impulse of human nature that relishes a challenge. The author, Garrett Lyons, is a former senior lecturer in mechanical and manufacturing engineering in Trinity College

Dublin. No one else has the combination of interests that would enable them to write this book – a profound interest in history; the expertise in engineering design required to explain the machinery involved; and a keen understanding of the local geography, having lived in the area all his life. The multidisciplinary university that is Trinity College is just the place to nurture these interests – a university where scholarship of this kind can be pursued for the love of learning itself.

Garrett Lyons, who came to work in Trinity in 1960, is known to all who have studied and taught engineering in the college over the past half-century. He was presented with a Festschrift volume, *Perspectives on Design and Bioengineering*, in 2008; in that volume, the late Professor John Fitzpatrick wrote of him: 'His devotion to the subject of design and the understanding of how things work have enabled him to imbue the capacity for critical thought in students.'

In this book on the Dublin and Kingstown railway we see that capacity in action in the analysis of an under-reported and sometimes undervalued feat of engineering innovation that resulted in a railway that many of us travel regularly. Indeed, the railway passes through the Grand Canal Dock area, now a byword for innovation and excellence in technology on a global scale, where many multinational technology companies have their European headquarters.

From this book we can all learn to appreciate that, in a former time, the Dublin and Kingstown railway was a wonder of engineering experimentation and design. Read this book and marvel.

Trinity College Dublin
July 2015

INTRODUCTION

Events during the 19th century, both at home and abroad, had a huge impact on Ireland and its population. The first such was the Act of Union, enacted on 1 August 1801, which brought an end to the Irish parliament by subsuming its powers into Westminster.

Article 6 of the act introduced free trade between the two islands, with an end to tariff protection for Irish produce. In the long term this had disastrous results for Irish manufactured goods. The exodus of Irish parliamentarians and their households also caused a huge social blight in Dublin. One consequence of this mass departure was the large number of empty properties slowly falling into decay and then becoming home to some of the worst slums in the British Isles. Dublin, which in 1800 was the second city of the empire, had slipped to tenth place by the end of the century. As housing and social problems worsened, many more affluent Dubliners moved to the newly created townships outside the old city. These townships, which included Rathmines-Rathgar, Pembroke, Clonskeagh, Kilmainham and Clontarf, ringed the city, their independence depriving Dublin Corporation of rates that might have been used for slum relief.

The Napoleonic wars were both good and bad for Ireland. Because England, alarmed by the Rebellion of 1798, feared another Jacobin uprising, some 100,000 troops were stationed in the country. On the plus side Ireland's manufactures – wool and rope, cloth for uniforms, pottery and agricultural produce – supplied the war effort. Cities such as Cork prospered as they became entrepôt ports for supply to the military. However, with the ending of these wars and the demand for military supplies, Cork and other centres such as Galway and Westport fell back into poverty.

Thirty years later Ireland was ravaged by what has come to be known as the Great Famine, its horrors greatly exacerbated by the large number of absentee landlords and the cruel behaviour of their agents. There were many acts of great charity by individuals, philanthropic societies and church committees but the British parliament's laissez faire attitude to the pitifully distressed country was shameful.

As the century drifted on the effects of the Act of Union and of absentee landordism on the rural poor and their slum-dwelling city brothers and sisters saw a great percentage of the population living in sociocultural subjugation and grinding poverty. Thackeray's *Irish Sketchbook* (1843) and Kohl's *Travels in Ireland* (1844) present a sad picture of a nation in decline. Although the socioeconomic gap between the poor and the gentry was equally bad in England a religious divide in Ireland served to worsen its effects. As a result we find many history books on 19th-century Ireland devoted entirely to the catastrophic effects of the Famine, political disturbances and the soul-destroying results of social deprivation in Dublin and other cities.

But in the Victorian era there was another Ireland where great architectural and civil/mechanical engineering works were undertaken. Many of these are beautifully illustrated in Michael Barry's *Victorian Dublin Revealed* (2011) and Peter Pearson's *Between the Mountains and the Sea* (2007). This little book of mine is an attempt to look at one such endeavour, Ireland's first railway. I hope it gives some sense of the times and of the achievement.

ILLUSTRATIONS
AND MAPS

ABBREVIATIONS

Dublin and Kingstown Railway	D&KR
Dublin Penny Journal	*DPJ*
Engineers Ireland	EI
Grace's Guide	*GG*
Illustrated London News	*ILN*
Irish Railway Record Society	IRRS
National Library of Ireland	NLI
Royal Society of Antiquaries of Ireland	RSAI
Science Museum UK	SMUK
Walker's Hibernian Magazine	*WHM*

Fig. 1.1   Henry Brocas Junior, 'Wreck of the *Rochdale* at Seapoint Martello Tower' (*WHM*, 1807).   19

Fig. 1.2   John Rennie the elder (1761-1821).   20

Fig. 2.1   Charles Blacker Vignoles (1793-1875).   29

Fig. 2.2   William Dargan (1799-1867).   31

Fig. 2.3   The first train leaves Westland Row (courtesy NLI).   33

Fig. 3.1   Cross-section of the road embankment and walls (courtesy EI).   37

Fig. 3.2   Cross-sections of the D&KR embankments from Serpentine Avenue to Blackrock (courtesy EI).   39

Fig. 3.3   The Lees cutting and bridge (courtesy NLI).   45

Fig. 3.4   Ordnance bridge and cutting, Seapoint (courtesy IRRS).   46

Fig. 3.5   Cross-section of bridges (courtesy EI).   46

Fig. 3.6   Cross-section of the embankment in Seapoint (author's drawing).   47

Fig. 3.7   The Kingstown extension (courtesy RSAI).   48

Fig. 3.8   Proposed route of the line past the Martello tower (courtesy RSAI).   50

Fig. 3.9   Old Harbour embankment, *c.* 1900 (courtesy NLI).   51

Fig. 3.10 The original façade of Westland Row station house, 1834 (*DPJ*).   52

Fig. 3.11 Plan of Westland Row station house *c.* 1835 (author's drawing).   53

Fig. 3.12 The Old Coffee House, Dunleary (courtesy NLI).   54

Fig. 3.13 Kingstown Station from the Pavilion Gardens *c.* 1890 (courtesy NLI). 55

Fig. 3.14 Exterior (1970) and interior views of Blackrock Station
(courtesy IRRS and NLI).   56

Fig. 3.15 Salthill Station and Salthill Hotel *c.* 1870 (courtesy NLI).   60

Fig. 3.16 Blackrock Baths *c.* 1900.   64

Fig. 3.17 Images of Salthill Hotel showing the footbridge and derelict baths
(courtesy NLI).   65

Fig. 4.1   The rail and sleeper system of the early railways (author's drawing). 68

Fig. 4.2   Granite sleepers accommodating crossing rails (author's drawing). 69

Fig. 4.3   A D&KR rail chair assembly and granite sleepers, drilled for chair
mounting (courtesy IRRS).   70

Fig. 4.4   Chaired rail with supports (author's drawing).   73

Fig. 4.5   Cross-section of bridge rail pinned to sleepers (author's drawing). 73

Fig. 4.6   Cross-section of Vignoles's flanged rail (author's drawing).   73

Fig. 4.7   Vignoles's flat-bottomed rail held with Pandrol clips
(courtesy M. Smith).   75

Fig. 4.8   Semaphore signals (author's drawing).   77

Fig. 5.1   Sharp Roberts locomotive *Experiment* (author's drawing).   80

Fig. 5.2   The D&KR-built locomotive *Princess* (courtesy Debra Wenlock). 83

Fig. 5.3 a) A D&KR closed second-class carriage showing Bergin's buffer. 85

Fig. 5.3 b) A D&KR third-class carriage.   85

Fig. 6.1   An atmospheric train leaving Kingstown station (branch platform). 90

Fig. 6.2   The Magdeburg experiment.   91

Fig. 6.3 a) The principle of atmospheric propulsion (author's drawing). 93

Fig. 6.3 b) The principle of atmospheric propulsion (author's drawing). 93

Fig. 6.4   Drawing of valves and carriage in Samuda and Clegg's

        patent application (author's drawing).   97

Fig. 6.5   Sketch of the leather strip valve (author's drawing).   98

Fig. 6.6   Section of tube showing the continuous slot (author's drawing).   99

Fig. 6.7   Sketch of tube showing the leather valve in place (*GG*).   100

Fig. 6.8   First dispatch of mail bags to Euston Station, London (courtesy *ILN*). 101

Fig. 6.9   The boundaries of the Board of Ordnance land

        at Battery No 12, Glastoole (author's drawing).   105

Fig. 6.10 Walker's preferred layout for the atmospheric line (author's drawing). 107

Fig. 6.11 Walker's design for the openings in the over-cover (author's drawing). 109

Fig. 6.12 The pumping house and ponds in Kingstown,

        looking towards Dublin.   112

Fig. 6.13 Cross-section of layout for Dalkey Atmospheric Railway

        (author's drawing).   114

Fig. 7.1   The 1884 façade of Westland Row Station.   127

Fig. 7.2   The general floor plan of Westland Row Station and lines as of 1886

        (author's drawing).   128

Fig. 7.3   Details of the rail system in Kingstown Station *c.* 1907

        (author's drawing).   129

Fig. 7.4   The mail-packet station on Carlisle Pier *c.* 1908.   131

MAPS

Map 1.1 Cubitt's 1833 proposal for a Dublin-Kingstown ship canal

        (author's drawing).   18

Map 1.2 Map, drawn in 1817, showing Old Dunleary,

        its harbour and the new harbour's east pier.   21

Map 1.3 Kingstown Harbour in 1837.   22

Map 2.1 The line of the railway as of 1834 (red) and extension

        to the present station, 1837 (blue).   28

Map 3.1 The line of the D&KR from Westland Row to Booterstown.   40

Map 3.2 The line of the D&KR from Booterstown to Dunleary.   41

Map 6.1 The tramway from the east pier to Dalkey Quarry.   102

Map 6.2 The complete tramway, 1834 (in red).   102

Map 6.3 The locations of the track and buildings
of the Dalkey Atmospheric Railway (author's drawing).   111

Map 7.1 The Harcourt Street line *c.* 1887.   125

Appendix I

Fig. 1 Original frontage of Westland Row Station (author's drawing).   137

Fig. 2 Train leaving Westland Row.   137

Fig. 3 The Sharp, Roberts locomotive *Hibernia* (courtesy SMUK).   144

Fig. 4 D&KR second-class carriage.   144

Fig. 5 The Forrester engine *Vauxhall* (courtesy SMUK).   146

Plate I From Blackrock looking towards Williamstown and Merrion.   140

Plate II Lord Cloncurry's bridge and 'bathing temple'.   140

Plate III Sir Harcourt Leexs's cutting and overbridge.   141

Plate IV From the footbridge at Seapoint Hotel looking towards Salthill.   141

Plate V From the Martello tower (Ordnance) bridge in Seapoint
looking towards Kingstown.   142

Appendix II

Fig. 1 Bergin's spring buffer.   149

CHAPTER 1

Why the Dublin and Kingstown Railway?

The Significance of Kingstown Harbour

While sitting on the DART, comfortably whizzing towards Blackrock, I often wonder how many of my fellow passengers think of the previous life of the railroad they travel along, its early engines, the men who brought it into being, the excitement it caused and the number of world firsts it achieved. This railway prompted the book you are now reading.

We must start with the Dublin and Kingstown Railway (D&KR) which began operations in December 1834. It was the first steam loco-motive passenger railway in Ireland (only the second in the world) and the first to join a capital city to a main port, in this case the new Kingstown Harbour, said by some to be the finest artificial harbour in Europe.

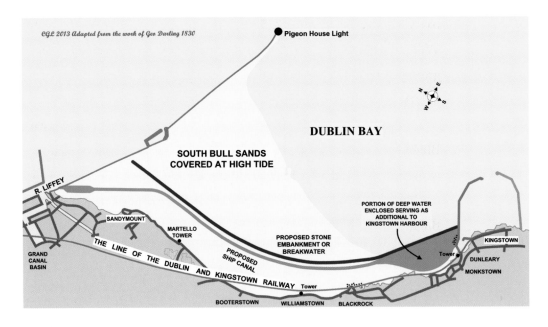

Pigeon House Light

DUBLIN BAY

SOUTH BULL SANDS COVERED AT HIGH TIDE

R. LIFFEY

SANDYMOUNT

MARTELLO TOWER

PORTION OF DEEP WATER ENCLOSED SERVING AS ADDITIONAL TO KINGSTOWN HARBOUR

KINGSTOWN

GRAND CANAL BASIN

THE LINE OF THE DUBLIN AND KINGSTOWN RAILWAY

PROPOSED SHIP CANAL

PROPOSED STONE EMBANKMENT OR BREAKWATER

Tower

DUNLEARY

MONKSTOWN

Tower

BOOTERSTOWN   WILLIAMSTOWN   BLACKROCK

Map 1.1: Cubitt's 1833 proposal for a Dublin-Kingstown ship canal.

From childhood I was well aware of the magic of steam travel and had the good fortune to experience some two decades of it before its extinction in Ireland. The name 'Kingstown' was also quite familiar to me as I had a number of venerable maiden aunts who never ceased to call it this, rather than Dún Laoghaire, the name to which it permanently changed at the foundation of the Irish Free State in 1921-2.

In order to explain the importance of a link between Dublin and Kingstown Harbour we must look to the problems of the port of Dublin. Because of silting and moving sandbars, navigation by ships of two hundred tons or more in the port of Dublin was dangerous, so insurance charges on ships 'for Dublin' were set high. This meant that, even though the capital city was well connected by canal to the interior of the country, the problems of the port meant that cargo ships often unloaded on to lighters in the bay, while steam passenger and mail ships berthed at the Pigeon House and later in Howth Harbour. To solve the problems of the bay Captain John Perry (1725), Sir Thomas Page (1800)[1] and later Sir William Cubitt (see Map 1.1) made suggestions for the construction of great ship canals into the port of Dublin, albeit from different originating points.

After completing his survey of Dublin Bay (1800-1), Captain Bligh[2] spoke trenchantly in opposition to the concept of a ship canal. He wrote: 'A canal and the Liffey would destroy each other as both would be too burdensome to keep up and the general bias would go to the latter.' Bligh believed that the canal would fail in the long run – but not before financially ruining the port of Dublin.

In addition Dublin Bay was feared and loathed by mariners. Its combination of sandy beaches from Ringsend to Blackrock and craggy rocks thereafter, along with the dangers of north-eastern gales, made it a place of loss both of life and of shipping. Numerous voices were repeatedly raised about this matter, reaching a peak in 1807, after the loss of the sloop *Prince of Wales* and the sailing brig *Rochdale* in a fearsome winter storm on 19 November.[3] These and others troop ships had set sail from Ringsend to transport members of the Cork and Mayo regiments of militia to

1   G. Corry, 'The Dublin Bar: The Obstacle to the Improvement of the Port of Dublin', *Dublin Historical Record*, Vol. 30, No. 4, 1970, pp. 137-52.

2   G. Corry and G. Daly, 'Captain William Bligh in Dublin, 1800-1801', *Dublin Historical Record*, Vol. 44, No. 1, 1991, pp. 20-33.

3   See E.J. Burke, 'The Sinking of the *Rochdale* and the *Prince of Wales*', *Dublin Historical Record*, Vol. 6, No. 2, 2008, pp. 129-35.

Fig. 1.1: 'Wreck of the Rochdale *at Seapoint Martello Tower' (Henry Brocas Junior).*

Fig. 1.2: *John Rennie the elder (1761-1821).*

the Peninsular War. The *Prince of Wales* was wrecked on the rocks below Maretimo House and the *Rochdale* at the Martello tower in Seapoint. Other ships from Dublin perished on this night and the total loss of lives is estimated at four hundred. Corpses were washed up on the strands of Dublin Bay for a number of days. Their remains lie in graveyards at St Begnet's Dalkey and in Merrion Road (by the Tara Towers Hotel).

Public outcry about this loss of life finally prompted action and in 1813 an act of parliament ordered the building of an 'asylum harbour' for the safety of ships. Unfortunately Howth was decided upon as the site and a harbour was duly created there. This work was under the control of John Rennie the elder (1761-1821)[4], even though Rennie had advised against Howth and for Dunleary in 1802.

When it was completed Howth Harbour was designated the official harbour for the mails (postal service) but problems soon arose. Because of silting, the draught within the harbour walls was insufficient for later mail

4   John Rennie, a farmer's younger son, was born in East Lothian, Scotland, and showed an aptitude for mechanics at a very early age. As a child he spent much time in the workshop of Andrew Meikle, the inventor of the threshing machine. From 1780-3 he studied in the University of Edinburgh. After spending some time working with steam engineer James Watt in Staffordshire, in 1791 he started in business as a mechanical engineer on his own account in Blackfriars in London, where he and his successors conducted engineering operations of vast importance.

packet ships and its rocky bottom precluded dredging. Another solution had to be found.

Again as a result of agitation by powerful voices, particularly a Captain Richard Toutcher, a site was chosen along the coast south of the city at the small fishing port of Dunleary (the fort of King Leary) which since ancient times had been a port for traffic with Wales. Here was a small harbour with a short pier built in 1758-68 (the 'Old Pier' on maps) to replace a ruinous medieval one. (The rebuilding cost of £20,000 was lower by £1000 than the estimate – rare indeed for an Irish construction project.)

The construction work was overseen by General Charles Vallencey, a military engineer, who advised that a single pier would soon become silted up by the sands of the bay that were washed in on the tides. He advocated the building of a dry wall at the Chicken Rocks as a remedy but this was never done. 'Old' Dunleary Harbour became a port of asylum for ships in the bay but by the end of the 18th century it had become less effective because of the reduction of the draught within the harbour as a result of silting.

An act of parliament of 1816 authorised the building of a great

Map 1.2: Old Dunleary, its harbour and the new harbour's east pier, from a map drawn in 1817.

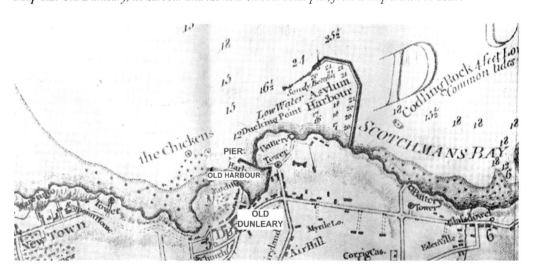

new harbour in Dunleary. Originally it was intended that only one pier (the east pier), 3500 feet (915 metres) long, would be built at the Codling Rock. However, when John Rennie was appointed directing engineer for the work, he insisted that a single pier would result in sand drifting behind it and to prevent this occurring he recommended that two piers be constructed. To prevent silting he called for a west pier 4950 feet (1520 metres) long at the Chicken Rocks as well as the east pier. In 1820 royal sanction was granted to an act of parliament for 'Construction of a West Pier'. Rennie was correct as the sand has since built up behind the west pier.

This pair of piers effectively embraced the old harbour of Dunleary (see Map 1.3). Rennie wanted the harbour to be 430 feet wide but he was overruled by the Harbour Commissioners and it was built at 1066 feet. This was clearly too wide to control the swells within the harbour and its width was subsequently reduced to 760 feet (232 metres).

Map 1.3: Kingstown Harbour in 1837.

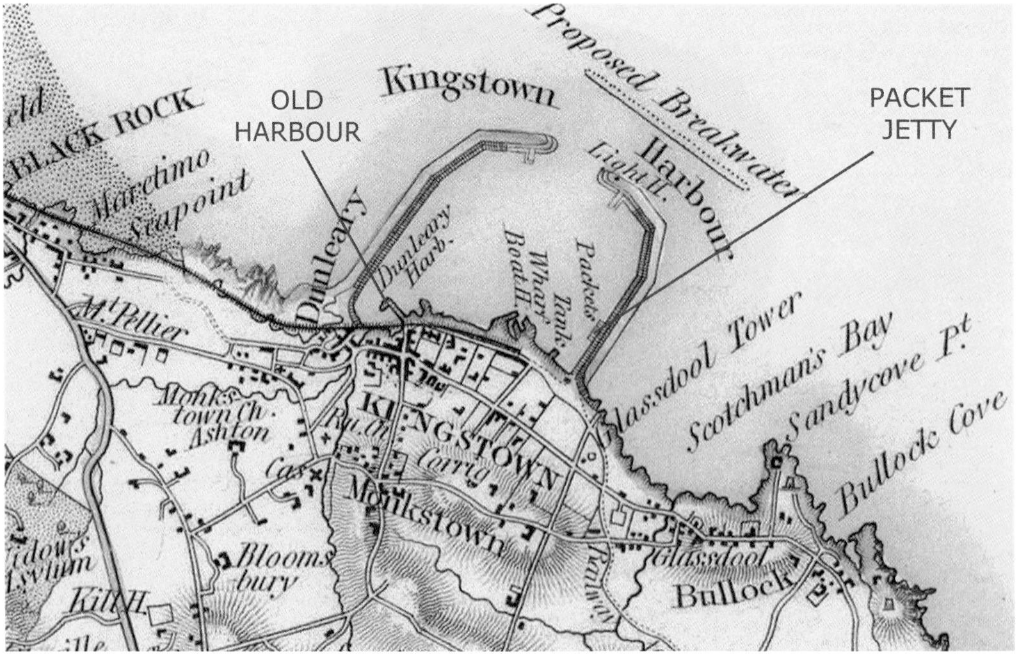

The Lord Lieutenant, Earl Whitworth, laid the foundation stone for the east pier in 1817. Behind it were set a coin of the realm, an inscription and the newspapers of the ten previous days. The construction material was Dalkey Hill granite, which was provided by Richard Toutcher, a long-time campaigner for the new harbour, at crippling cost to himself but none to the construction effort.

The new harbour was initially called Dunleary but was renamed the 'Royal Harbour of Kingstown' in 1821 on the occasion of the departure of George IV from the harbour at the end of a visit to Ireland. Later acts of parliament determined that the 'grounds about Dun Leary Harbour be transferred to the Commissioners of Kingstown Harbour' and that 'the Old Harbour and the New Harbour are but one, under the title of the Royal Harbour of Kingstown'. The bay formed between Dún Laoghaire Harbour and the Forty Foot is still known as 'Scotsman's Bay', in honour of John Rennie.

Now Ireland had a ready and safe means of ship communication with Britain, both for passengers and for mails. In 1826 the steam mail packet ships were officially transferred to Kingstown.

But what of the connection between Kingstown and Dublin? Again, proposals for a great ship canal to run along the coast to the Ringsend docks were mooted. Such a canal would cost an estimated £405,000 (€480,000)[5] an outrageously large, even unconscionable sum of money in the early 1800s.

The *House of Commons Journal* of 9 February 1825 noted:

A petition by several Gentlemen, Merchants Traders, freeholders, and others, of Dublin, was presented and read: setting forth, that by levels and surveys lately made, it appears practicable to make or maintain a railway or tramroad from the Royal Harbour of

---

5   To convert to present-day value multiply the sum in Euro by 120. Thus €480,000 becomes €57,600,000. (This is an approximate value.)

Kingstown in the parish of Monkstown in the County of Dublin, to or near Mount Street, in the city of Dublin, which would be of great public utility…

The scene was set for the Dublin & Kingstown Railway.

CHAPTER 2

THE DUBLIN AND KINGSTOWN RAILWAY

The Company, Its Development and Its Personnel

O n foot of the 1825 petition a bill was submitted to parliament which, as was usually the case, provoked a storm of protest. Businesses such as the Grand Canal Company, which had strong financial interests in the possibility of a ship canal, and wealthy landowners who wished their sea views and amenities to be preserved lobbied parliament and successfully brought about the defeat of the bill. Another attempt was made in 1827 and again the Grand Canal Company objected. This time it overplayed its hand, causing parliament to be better disposed to the concept of a railway.

Little progress towards the construction of a canal had taken place and this stimulated some shareholders of the Grand Canal Company and others to look to alternatives. Some of these individuals were members of the Society of Friends (Quakers) who through their connections knew of the success of the world's first railway, the Stockton and Darlington, which, because so many Quaker businessmen were involved in it, was known as the 'Quakers' Line'[1]. One of the Grand Canal Company shareholders, James Pim Junior, had already funded a survey for a railway from Dublin to Kingstown, undertaken by the great Scottish civil engineer Alexander Nimmo (1783-1832). Nimmo's work, completed in early 1831, encouraged Pim and other Dublin businessmen to form a committee to pursue the goal of a railway connection.

A second petition was submitted to parliament on 28 February 1831 and, after much debate, assessment and political ping-pong, leave was granted to present a bill for the railway. Eventually, on 6 September 1831, this bill passed and received the royal assent (William IV, Cap. 69), as did other acts (1 and 2 William IV, Cap. 33) to incorporate the Dublin and Kingstown Railway Company. In this way the company became a corporate entity.

It cost the D&KR Company £1626/14s/2d to move the bill through parliament. The businessmen got most of what they wanted but two clauses of the bill were worrying. One, which related to land dealing, refused them rights of compulsory purchase in relation to two landowners whose properties lay along the line. These were the Second Baron Cloncurry and the Reverend Sir Harcourt Lees, who lived at Maretimo and Blackrock House respectively and of whom more later on.

The other clause, which was more menacing for the businessmen, stated that in the event of the construction of a ship canal along the same route no compensation would be granted to the railway company. Fortunately for the D&KR any belief in a ship canal faded away within a relatively short time. However, the Grand Canal Company continued to trouble the D&KR's fundraising efforts.

A copy of the bill was circulated to all D&KR shareholders and a meeting was duly held in Dublin Chamber of Commerce, Commercial

---

1   A full 73 per cent of the shareholders of this line were Quakers. See A. Prior, and M. M. Kirby, 'The Society of Friends and the Family Firm, 1700-1830', *Business History* 35, 4 (1993), pp. 66-85 (Taylor and Francis).

Buildings, Dame Street, on 25 November 1831. At this meeting several important decisions were made, including the election of a board of directors for the company. The officers elected were: Thomas Pim (Chairman); Edward Alexander; John Barton; James Ferrier; Joseph Kincaid; James Perry; Robert Roe and James Twigg.[2] It was also decided to apply to the Commissioners of Public Works in Ireland for a loan of £100,00, two-thirds of the estimated cost of the railway.[3]

James Pim Junior (1796-1856), who was appointed company secretary, had previously been secretary to the provisional committee of the D&KR group. He came from a wealthy family and was a partner in Boyle, Low and Pim, stockbrokers and banking agents in Dublin. He was also an agent for the Imperial Insurance Company and a shareholder in the Grand Canal Company. He was elected a life member of the Royal Irish Academy in 1839. Pim began correspondence with the Commissioners of Public Works to request the loan. The Commissioners responded with an offer of £50,000 and then began a year of careful correspondence by Pim during which he gradually and cleverly moved the Commissioners to a final amount of £75,000. In September 1832 the Lords of HM Treasury sanctioned the loan and the Commissioners informed Pim on 7 November.[4] The D&KR was ready to begin work on the railway.

The first plan was to begin the railway at Thomas Clarendon's riding school, 200 Great Brunswick Street (now Pearse Street). This would have meant an elevated railway running from a position approximately in line with the back of New Square in Trinity, along the back of the houses and then along the edge of the university's College Park, a route

---

2   Edward Alexander and James Perry, as well as both Pims, were Quakers. This followed the pattern of significant Quaker involvement in the world's first railway, the Stockton and Darlington, which began in 1826.

3   The Commission of Public Works in Ireland was created in 1831 by act of parliament (1 and 2 William IV, Cap. 33) and empowered to make loans for various improvements to the infrastructure of the country. Railways and canals were included in its remit.

4   All this correspondence is contained in House of Commons papers, HC 291, Vol. 35, Sub-vol. 1, 1833.

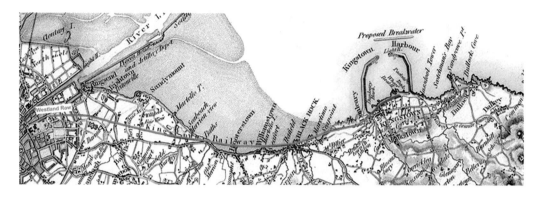

Map 2.1: The line of the railway as of 1834 (red) and extension to the present station, 1837 (blue).

totally unacceptable to the affected parties. As a result of objections from the board of TCD and nearby property owners the company chose an alternative site near the corner of Great Brunswick Street and Westland Row. The line would run from Westland Row to the Old Harbour, the edge of Kingstown's west pier in Salthill. (See Map 2.1, red line)

The new D&KR board also announced that it had undertaken surveys to assess the amount of commercial and passenger traffic on Rock Road through Booterstown, Williamstown, Blackrock and on to Kingstown, then a rapidly growing new town (see Appendix IV). The directors confidently estimated a potential income of £29,300 per annum, while the estimated cost of running the line was £10,000 per annum. Furthermore the company planned to create public swimming baths in Blackrock and Salthill and to encourage the 'higher classes of society to avail themselves of the peculiar advantages of the railway…[so that] Kingstown will become a spot where all classes will be attracted by the opportunity for healthy exercise amidst a pure atmosphere and beautiful and romantic surroundings.' Clearly there was money to be made and by 1836 the value of the company's shares had risen from £60 to £84.[5]

In 1832 James Pim was appointed company treasurer and replaced as secretary by Thomas Fleming Bergin, an engineer. He and Pim were to

5. The *Dublin Penny Journal*, Vol. 4, No. 182, 26 December 1835, pp. 203-5.

prove two of the most valuable engines the D&KR possessed, although other individuals also played an important part.

The Commissioners of Public Works had agreed to advance a loan of £75,000 but this did not come without attendant conditions. The interest rate was 4 per cent and repayments of £2500 per annum were to begin at the end of the first year. The first tranche of the loan – £50,000 – would not be advanced until the D&KR had spent an equal amount of its own capital. It was to be a no-frills project, all building work simple and free of any unnecessary elaboration. The Commissioners also suggested that a skilled engineer should review the plans made by Alexander Nimmo, who had died in January 1832, eventually nominating Charles Blacker Vignoles (1793-1875). Born in Wexford, Vignoles was one of Ireland's greatest engineers. He had previously had a military career and had developed an enduring friendship with the then chairman of the Commissioners of Public Works, Major General Sir John Fox Burgoyne, himself a military engineer. Their friendship greatly helped the fortunes of the D&KR.

The company immediately appointed Vignoles as its chief engineer and by 24 March 1832 he had drawn up final plans for the railway, the total cost of which was to be £126,406/11s. During 1832 Vignoles made some forty visits to Ireland. He and the likeable James Pim spent much time walking and assessing the proposed route and became lifelong friends; this

Fig. 2.1: *Charles Blacker Vignoles (1793-1875).*

also helped the smooth development of the railway.

In later years Richard Pim (in 1841) and Samuel Haughton (in 1849) (not to be confused with the eminent scientist, Samuel Haughton FTCD) were promoted to the positions of mechanical engineer and inspector of works to the D&KR. In 1849 Haughton, while acting as superintendent of the engine factory, developed the friction sledge for stopping locomotives.[6] This device earned him a gold medal from the Royal Dublin Society. Although the D&KR did not put it to use, the concept of the friction sledge can still be seen at railway termini where friction buffers are used. When the D&KR was leased to the Dublin and Wicklow Railway, Haughton became locomotive superintendent and remained in this position until his retirement in 1864. Richard Pim oversaw the construction of Ireland's first 'home built' locomotive.

In 1832 the D&KR could at last go to tender for the construction of the line and its stations. At this point another important character entered the story. Carlow-born William Dargan was an engineer, an entrepreneur and a great philanthropist. He made his name working with the renowned Thomas Telford on the construction of the road from London to Holyhead and the Menai Bridge and was a famous and wealthy man by the mid-1840s. The D&KR was Dargan's debut in railway construction and his tender for the work at £83,000 was the lowest presented. Dargan made contractual commitments to carry out Vignoles's plans and specifications and also to maintain the work 'in good order' for two years. He contracted to build a line of 5 miles 43 chains and 4 yards (9 km) with all underbridges and overbridges, embankments, cuttings, fillings, ballast and stone sleepers and to lay the track. All work was to be completed and the line ready for use by 1 June 1834. A penalty of £100 for each week of delay would apply, as well as a bonus of £50 for every week in advance of the due date that the work was completed. Dargan's previous experience in building a roadway

---

6   See Samuel W. Haughton, 'Account of Experiments Made on a New Friction Sledge for Stopping Railway Trains', *The Transactions of the Royal Irish Academy*, Vol. 22, 1849, pp. 219-21.

Fig. 2.2: *William Dargan (1799-1867),*
businessman, railway king and patron of the arts.
Ireland's National Gallery was founded in his honour.

across the Stanley Sands in Holyhead proved invaluable when the D&KR line was laid from Merrion to Blackrock as, later on, after the construction of the line, did his freely-given advice on the operation of the line.[7]

Work on the D&KR began at Salthill on 11 April 1833 and by 31 July one of the lines was completed. Some of the directors and their friends made the first journey along the line in a coach drawn by horse power. On 4 October the locomotive *Vauxhall* drew a few carriages to Williamstown and back to Westland Row. Full-length journeys took place on 9 October. *Saunders Newsletter* of 1833 tells us the journeys were under the supervision of Thomas Bergin and ran from Westland Row Station house to Salthill and back. The first train, drawn by the engine *Hibernia*, carried a large number of invited guests, among them the Earl of Longford, in one first-class, three second-class and five third-class carriages. The engine was not perfectly adjusted as one piston rod was one-eighth of an inch (3 mm) longer than the other. The rails were also said to be in 'bad order due to wet', which caused increased friction. Journey times of nineteen minutes fifteen seconds out and twenty-three minutes back were achieved and the passengers declared themselves delighted with the novel experience. There was much comment on the efficacy of Mr Bergin's as yet unpatented spring

---

7   For a full description of William Dargan's life and career see F. Mulligan, *William Dargan: An Honourable Life*, Dublin: Lilliput Press, 2013.

buffers to 'ward off the concussion' between carriages when the train came to a halt. A further passenger-carrying trip was made on the same day, this time employing the locomotive *Vauxhall*. This engine again exhibited some faults and the journey times were fourteen minutes thirty seconds out and twenty-two minutes thirty seconds back.

Thus the first train journeys in Ireland were made and the board of D&KR set a provisional date of 22 October 1834 for the opening of the line. This target was not met and on 7 November flood debris in the Dodder destroyed the new railway bridge over the river. Work began to make good the flood damage by building a new wooden bridge and this was completed by the last days of November. On Tuesday 16 December 1834 Dublin newspapers carried this notice:

DUBLIN AND KINGSTOWN RAILWAY
WILL BE OPENED

For the conveyance of passengers
On tomorrow (Wednesday) 17th instant

A train of carriages will start from each end of the line every hour from nine o'clock am till four o'clock in the afternoon (both inclusive) at the following fares:
In the First Class Carriage: One Shilling*
In the Second Class Carriage: Eight Pence
In the Third Class Carriage: Six Pence
Every train will include carriages of each class and will stop at the company's station house, Black-rock, both going and returning, to take up and set down passengers, and in a short time it is intended to stop at other places for the same purposes. Parcels will be conveyed from Westland Row to Blackrock and Kingstown at the following rates:-
Not exceeding one cwt: fourpence
Exceeding one cwt and not exceeding five cwt: one shilling.
No train to start between eleven o'clock and half-past two on Sundays.

T.F. Bergin
Clerk of the Company
Westland-row Dec 13th 1834

* £1 = 20 shillings. One shilling (1s) = twelve old pence (12d). One penny = €0.005

Fig. 2.3: *The first train leaves Westland Row Station.*
Illustration by John Harris (1791–1873), after an original by Andrew Nicholl.

At 9.00 on the morning of 17 December the engine *Hibernia* steamed out of Westland Row, pulling the first train filled with 'very fashionable passengers' (*see* Fig. 2.3). It was one of nine trains that ran throughout the day. Six of the trains drew nine coaches, the remainder drew eight and all were described as 'full to overflowing'. Some five thousand passengers travelled on this inaugural day.

At the end of the day the company's directors and their friends took themselves to the new D&KR-owned Salthill Hotel in Dún Laoghaire for a great celebration, which continued until 4.00 the following morning.

Of course the railway was more than an exciting piece of engineering. It had to make money and indeed it did. The figures speak for themselves. F. Whishaw inspected the books in 1839 and reported: 'In the years 1834 to 1836 the number of trips performed by the engines amounted to 29,613, a distance of 167,807 miles (268,500 km); the consumption

Year ending	Passengers	Receipts	Receipts and expenditure year ending 28 February 1839	
1836	1,123,971	£30,992/11s/2d	Passenger traffic	£34,408/17s/0d
1837	1,184,428	£32,138/9s/4d	Parcel traffic	£307/9s/8d
1838	1,243,972	£33,880/7s/8d	Baths net	£91/7s/0d
1839	1,326,830	£35, 307 13s/8d	Post Office contract	£500/0s/0d
1840	1,280,763	£34,175/15s/5d	Total	£35,307/13s/8d
			Expenditure for period	£20,453/15s/3d
			Gross profit for year	£14,853/18s/5d

Table 2.1: Data from the books of Dublin and Kingstown Railway, 1836–40.

of coke being 4,347,573 lbs (2,070,270 kg). Mr Bergin [Thomas Bergin, engineer and secretary of the company] reckons that the profitable load, taking the average of the passenger trains on the railway, is only about ¼₄th of the gross load.'

The data from D&KR books, reproduced in Table 2.1 above, shows how traffic increased steadily in the years 1836-40.[8] The growth in revenue between 1836 and 1837 shows the effect of increasing the second-class fare from eightpence to ninepence. In fact the D&KR was one of the most profitable passenger railways in the British Isles.

8   See F. Whishaw, *The Railways of Great Britain and Ireland. Practically Described and Illustrated* (2nd edition), London: John Weale, 1842.

CHAPTER 3

The Permanent Way and Its Stations

Dublin to Booterstown; Booterstown to Kingstown

I hope the reader will forgive me for jumping from 1834 to the 1900s in order to explain the situation with regard to the stations along the line. This is necessary to give some of the salient facts.

The initial act of parliament stated that the D&KR terminus at Kingstown would be 'to the east of the west pier and at the mouth of the Old Harbour', that is, just beyond Salthill. This was so even though the Liverpool and Holyhead steam packets calling to 'Dublin' twice daily had begun to use the harbour by berthing at a wooden jetty on the east pier (see Map 1.3). However, it had been decided that a special wharf for their use should be constructed at the west side of the harbour. Then it was determined that the draft in that part of the harbour would be unsuitable for larger steam packets and that a new wharf should be built approximately half a mile to the east and in deeper water. This made better connection with the roads of the burgeoning new town and was at the coastal end of the Forty Foot Road (later Sussex Parade, then Royal Marine Road and finally Marine Road). Therefore the railway needed to extend to the new wharf (from 1849 Victoria Wharf[1]) and have its station house near there.

Consequently, in March 1833, the board of D&KR prepared a bill allowing for the extension to the line and covering other matters, including sanction for the line to go on to Dalkey. Many people objected to this bill, some because they did not like the idea that a company which had not completed its first task should be seeking parliamentary approval for enlargement. Besides, who was to foot the bill? In the best Irish style the vested interests banded together to lobby against the extension. Among the individuals involved was Thomas Gresham[2], a businessman and owner of the Gresham Hotel in Dublin and the Royal (Marine) Hotel in Kingstown. Gresham, a shareholder in the D&KR, thought that if the line reached Dalkey the next step would be Bray, then a small fishing village but surrounded by beautiful scenery. He was sure that Bray would be developed as 'Ireland's Brighton' and that this would ruin his business.

There were others, including quarry owners, coaching businesses and jarvey-men,[3] who believed that the extension would damage their revenue.

The bill went to committee stage in parliament and had a very rough time. Daniel O'Connell spoke against it as yet another 'business bubble', worse than those that had gone before in the country. Running in the background of all this opposition was some dirty lobbying on the part, yet again, of the Grand Canal Company. Eventually the great O'Connell was brought on side (in no small measure because of the known honesty of Quakers in business dealings). Gresham's 'righteous opposition' was

---

1   Readers may view all the infrastructural changes at the pier and at other locations along the line 'as time passes' by using the valuable service supplied by Ordnance Survey Ireland at http://maps.osi.ie, that allows them to contrast the modern map with historic maps from 1837 and 1907.

2   Thomas Gresham was an enigmatic character. An English foundling child, he came to Ireland in search of employment as a very young man, eventually becoming butler to William Beauman of Rutland Square. In 1817 Gresham purchased 21-22 Sackville Street and began business there as a hotel owner. How he acquired the capital to undertake the enterprise is not known.

3   A Hiberno-English term for a hackney coachman, still in use in Killarney, County Kerry.

mitigated by the company's buying back for £400 some D&KR shares that he had purchased for £100 and he withdrew his objections.

There were other strands of opposition to be overcome before the bill was given royal assent in 1834: these are dealt with in the later section of this chapter entitled 'On to Kingstown'.

As the D&KR Company was heavily engaged in the construction of the line from Westland Row to Salthill nothing happened in Kingstown for some time.

THE ROAD

The D&KR line began from Westland Row Station house and ran at an elevated level. It was contained between support walls, progressively decreasing in height[4] until it reached Serpentine Avenue. The section to Barrow Street, which carried four lines, was 54 feet wide between parapets and from there to Serpentine Avenue it was 30 feet wide. The retaining

---

4   From Westland Row to Grand Canal Dock the descent is 1 in 440; it passes over the dock on a short plane. From there to the Circular Road (South Lotts Road) the slope is again 1 in 440, which continues until Sandymount Lane (now Avenue). It is then level until 400 metres from Salthill, from where it has a plane of ascent of 1 in 730 to Kingstown.

Fig. 3.1: Cross-section of the road embankment and walls (from Grierson).

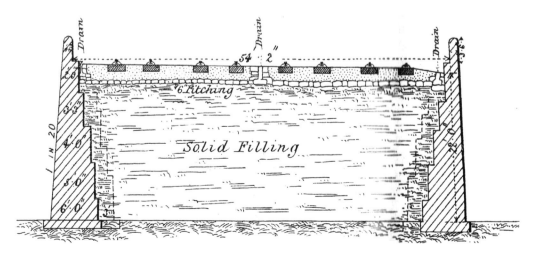

walls were of Donnybrook limestone, 6 feet thick at base, scaling to 2 feet 9 inches at the top (Fig. 3.1). The walls had a batter of 1 in 20. We must remember that much of the land through which the line passed had been the delta of the River Liffey in earlier times and so was somewhat unstable.

For economy the line's retaining walls were 'let in' to the soil for 9 inches (Fig. 3.2): this was perhaps not the best of Vignoles's decisions. Infilling between the walls progressed as they rose: a mixture of gravel from the Simmonscourt gravel pit (Map 3.2), earth and dredgings from the Liffey. It was compacted by heavy rolling, watering and a variety of other tricks. This compacting created a significant 'bursting' pressure against the retaining walls and some parts collapsed and had to be repaired and strengthened by a large number of iron cross-stays. The walls were inspected for many years but after the initial teething problems showed no signs of further deterioration. Improved land drainage in the area as a result of further work on the Liffey played no small part in ensuring the stability of the walls and embankment.

The Dublin Wide Streets Commissioners had a say in the design of the bridges over the streets along the line. They demanded that they have pedestrian openings on the pavements and be 30 feet in span on the roads. The bridges have an elliptical arc and some were built 'skew'[5], as the track was not always perpendicular to the line of the road. One has to be careful here as some bridges that have the appearance of skew are not truly so. Vignoles said the bridges 'were turned on the square or ordinary plan, with sufficiently long ring-stones and quoins where their faces were oblique to the direction of the retaining walls of the railway'.

The Vignoles-designed bridge over Grand Canal Dock had three spans and was truly skew; it was quite a wonder in its day. Where the Circular and Irishtown roads (now South Lotts Road and Bath Avenue) divided, the single bridge originally planned was changed to a pair. The one

---

5   See R. Gregory, 'The Art of Skew Bridges: the Technique and Its History Explored,' *The Journal of Architecture*, 16:5, 2001, pp. 615-74.

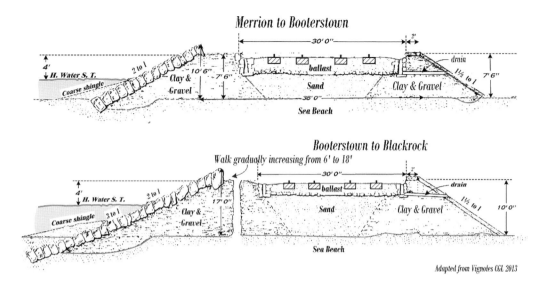

Merrion to Booterstown

Booterstown to Blackrock

Walk gradually increasing from 6' to 18'

Adapted from Vignoles CGL 2013

Fig. 3.2: *Cross-sections of the D&KR embankments from Serpentine Avenue to Blackrock.*

over the South Lotts Road is square while that over Bath Avenue is truly skewed, having an angle of 33°45'. These bridges have been strengthened by the fitting of iron beams over their arches, which are very low.

The bridge over the River Dodder had a chequered history. The first, a fine stone structure, was destroyed by flood and rapidly replaced by a wooden bridge so that the D&KR could meet its deadline for coming into operation. This bridge was designed by William Cubitt and lasted until 1847, when it was replaced by another timber structure. The third bridge had a short life as conditions on the Dodder were altered by the removal of the weir near Haig's Distillery (see Map 3.1). Increased 'water scour' on the bridge badly weakened it, so in 1851 a new iron bridge was built in its place. Barry Gibbons, the D&KR's engineer, designed the bridge, which rested on stone piers and had ironwork manufactured by William Fairbairn of Manchester. It was replaced in 1934 by the present very utilitarian steel one.

From Serpentine Avenue on to Blackrock the line ran on embankments with a ditch on either side (see Fig. 3.2). The embankment to

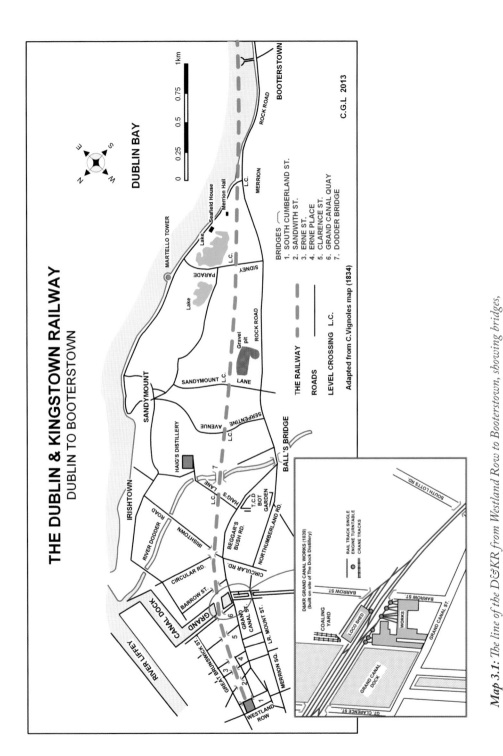

Map 3.1: *The line of the D&KR from Westland Row to Booterstown, showing bridges, the 1834 road structure and details of the Grand Canal Works.*

THE DUBLIN & KINGSTOWN RAILWAY
BOOTERSTOWN TO KINGSTOWN

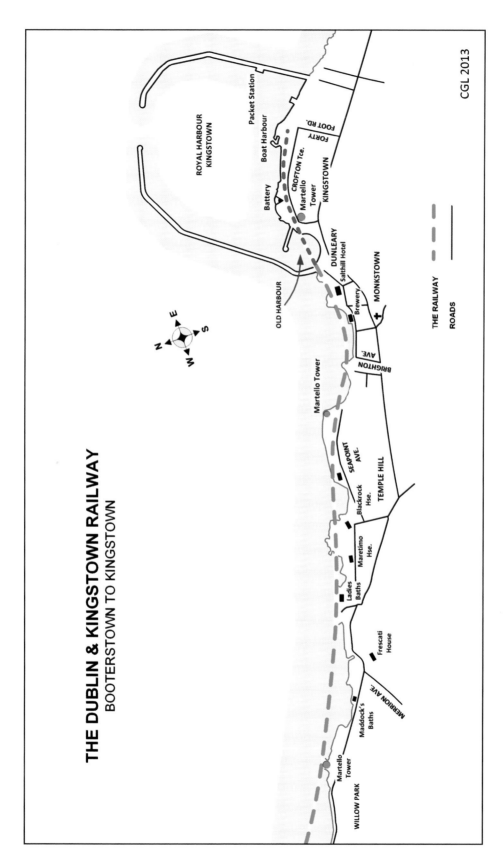

ROYAL HARBOUR
KINGSTOWN

Packet Station

Boat Harbour

Battery

CROFTON Tce.
Martello
Tower

FORTY
FOOT RD.

KINGSTOWN

DUNLEARY

Salthill Hotel

MONKSTOWN

Brewery

BRIGHTON
AVE.

OLD HARBOUR

Martello Tower

SEAPOINT
AVE.

Blackrock
Hse.

TEMPLE HILL

Maretimo
Hse.

Ladies
Baths

Frescati
House

MERRION AVE.

Maddock's
Baths

Martello
Tower

WILLOW PARK

THE RAILWAY

ROADS

CGL 2013

Map 3.2: The line of the D&KR from Booterstown to Kingstown.

Booterstown was some 7 feet 6 inches (2.2 metres) high. It was edged with hedging and passed the two marshy lakes and gravel pit (see Map 3.1). This pit provided much of the gravel needed for the embankments.

From Merrion the embankment went across the strand, going through dry land only in Williamstown and Blackrock. This section of the embankment was 10 feet (3 metres) in height and was difficult to construct in a stable manner. Fortunately Dargan had previous experience of this type of build.[6]

Each tide damaged the embankment until all the interstices in its seaward outer slope were filled and its face pitched and covered in boulders (see Fig. 3.2). The boulders were 1-12 cubic feet (0.028-0.34m^3) in dimension. During construction this section of the bank sank, at times quite alarmingly, and Vignoles ordered it be made one foot higher than the dimensions of Fig. 3.2. The parapets of the sea embankments were completed with granite stones whose seaward profile was parabolic, in order to reflect and absorb the force of waves.

This scheme worked – but not always. In 1836 a storm damaged a significant section of the embankment, which required rebuilding. On the advice of J.F. Burgoyne of the Commissioners of Public Works the parapets were raised after this storm. Unwanted granite sleepers were used as an extra protection. Over time the strand has risen along this whole section so wave action is no longer a problem. In Booterstown an embankment was built from the line to dry land (see Map 3.1), pierced by a culvert to allow the passage of water. This gave rail and strand access to the people of Booterstown village.

We have now reached Blackrock, where problems other than engineering ones had presented themselves as the D&KR had no compulsory purchase powers over the lands owned by Baron Cloncurry and Sir Harcourt Lees, that most unlikely partnership.

6   Working with Thomas Telford, the great Scottish engineer, Dargan had built a roadway across the Stanley Sands near Holyhead.

Valentine Brown Lawless, Second Baron Cloncurry, was born in 1773. He came from a family that in the space of two generations had, by means of politics and various shrewd moves – business, marriage, changing religion from Roman Catholicism to Anglicanism – come to amass a great fortune and significant estates.

Once he had graduated from TCD Valentine took the grand tour and on his return he became a member of the directory of the United Irishmen and a friend of Robert Emmet and Lord Edward Fitzgerald. After the disastrous rebellion of 1798 his political connections and pamphleteering against the proposed Act of Union resulted in his arrest. He was first incarcerated for some six weeks; then, in 1799, on foot of another pamphlet, rearrested and placed in the Tower of London. But the madness of King George III, which resulted in his inability to sign a writ sealing Valentine's imprisonment, meant that the latter gained his release in 1801. His father had died during his time in prison and the now Second Baron Cloncurry inherited Maretimo House, the 12,500-acre Lyons estate in County Kildare (income £12,000 per annum) and its beautiful house, Castle Lyons, lands in Meath and Mornington House off Merrion Square (now the Merrion Hotel). This last he disposed of, using the proceeds for the embellishment of his other houses.

Cloncurry later denied his connections with revolutionary politics but remained very liberal-minded. Although a Protestant, he was an ardent supporter of Catholic Emancipation. After Emancipation he gifted a site and moneys for the construction of the Catholic church of St John the Baptist in Blackrock and had installed at his expense the stained-glass main windows. Cloncurry was an outstandingly caring and generous landlord to the tenants on the Lyons estate and was also strongly and vociferously pro-Home Rule. Daniel O'Connell wrote of him: 'Ireland has not a better friend or one more devoted to her service than Lord Cloncurry. The poor man's justice of the peace; in private life the model of virtue; in public life worthy of the admiration and respect of the people.'

The Lees family came to Ireland with the Marquess of Townshend on his appointment as Lord Lieutenant in 1767. John Lees acted as Townshend's secretary and also served his successor, the Earl of Harcourt. He was later appointed secretary of the Irish Post Office – a position in which his son, Edward Smith Lees, succeeded him – and Gentleman Usher of the Black Rod in Ireland. By then a wealthy man, he built Blackrock House in 1774 and in 1804 he was created Baronet Lees of Blackrock.

Lees's son, Harcourt, was the eldest of six children. He read for his BA and later MA in Trinity College Cambridge and took Holy Orders in 1800. On his father's death in 1811 he succeeded to his baronetcy and to Blackrock House. But Lees was not just a Protestant clergyman: he was one of three assistant chaplains of the Grand Orange Lodge of Ireland and a bigot who hated the Roman Catholic Church and all its members. His vituperative anti-Roman pamphlets and letters (some twenty-five in all) were calculated to inflame anti-Catholic sentiment and to add strength to the clamour for the Act of Union. In the House of Commons Lees was attacked and quite effectively disgraced by Serjeant Perrin MP for his hypocritical behaviour: he had the benefice (£700 per annum) of Killaney, County Down, but never attended and installed a stipendiary curate to perform the services at a salary of £75 per annum.[7] Lees was also pilloried in several bawdy and amusing counter-pamphlets printed in Dublin.[8]

The story of Cloncurry and Lees is proof that the desire for social advantage and the prospect of free money can create the strangest of bedfellows. One must admire James Pim's courage in undertaking the task of negotiations with this pair, who must have loathed each other.

It appears that Lord Cloncurry was not well disposed even to the

7 'Speech of Mr Serjeant Perrin MP on the Motion of Lord Russel', on Monday March 30, 1835, Henry Hooper, 13 Pall Mall East, 1835 (House of Commons Committee on the Irish Church).

8 See 'A Poetic Epistle to the "Wild Huntsman", the Reverend Sir Harcourt Lees etc., Dublin', R Grace, Printer, Mary Street, 1821, and 'The Trial of Sir Harcourt Lees, Bart…on Charges of Barretry and Eaves-Dropping', Henry McPherson, Dublin, 1823.

Fig. 3.3: *The cutting and bridge on the estate of Harcourt Lees (looking towards Dublin).*

concept of the railway. In October 1832 he wrote to D&KR and to the Board of Works: 'I continue to believe that the proposed undertaking does not hold out such material and other probable benefits as should induce me to make the contemplated sacrifice.' However the railway needed to go through his estate at Maretimo and that of Lees at Blackrock House, so some agreement on this was necessary. The original intention, and the solution sanctioned by the act of parliament, was to deviate inland and construct a tunnel some 500 yards (460 metres) long, an extremely expensive operation. The board of D&KR had other ideas and James Pim gave neither Cloncurry nor Lees any rest in his attempts to achieve the railway company's objectives. As well as submitting designs for the ornamental masonry work on the section of the line that would cross the estates of Cloncurry and Lees, he had models made of its appearance.

Eventually Cloncurry and Lees capitulated and a bargain was struck. It was expensive for the D&KR but not as expensive as the long tunnel would have been, so everyone was happy. Cloncurry received a payment of £3000 and Lees £7500. Among the structural works granted them was an elegantly executed Doric over-bridge to give Cloncurry access from his home to the strand. This had two towers of Seapoint granite and an interlaced ironwork walkway (Appendix I, Plate II). Lees's land was divided by a short tunnel (70 feet), constructed by the 'cut and cover' method, with a walkway provided on it. They got a small boat harbour

Fig. 3.4: Ordnance bridge
and cutting, Seapoint.

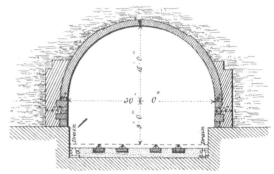

Fig. 3.5: Cross-section of
bridges (from Grierson).

(Vance's Harbour), a fishing pier, a Gothic summerhouse and a camera obscura tower in the grounds of Blackrock House. Also included was the development of a bathing place complete with a Grecian style 'bathing temple'[9]. The line could now progress through the small hill at the edge of the two estates by means of a cutting (see Fig. 3.3). With the creation of a short embankment (of the same specifications as before) to reach just past the present Seapoint Station, the line again ran on dry land.

From a point beginning approximately at Seapoint Terrace and ending at Seafield Avenue the curve of Seapoint Avenue had to be removed to make way for the railway.

A further cutting was made, over which a bridge to accommodate

9   These may be clearly seen in the 1907 OS map at http://maps.osi.ie. The present situation can be viewed using the 'satellite' view of the area in Google Maps.

Fig. 3.6: Cross-section of the embankment at Seapoint (adapted from Grierson).

the transfer of heavy ordnance to the Martello tower had to be constructed (see Fig. 3.4). This bridge and the one made for the estate of Harcourt Lees were of the same inner dimensions as the same form work was used for them (Fig. 3.5).

Another embankment followed (Fig. 3.6). Vignoles instructed Dargan to use a diving bell for its construction if necessary but this was not required. With the building of this embankment the line came to Salthill.

A route to Kingstown somewhat different from the one defined in the act had been undertaken. This was because the company already believed that its petition not to end at Salthill but to continue to the east pier would be successful. Therefore the D&KR deviated to the seaward side of Salthill House, so the final section of the line was cut through the hill on which the house stood. The spoil from removing part of the hill was used to fill embankments. The line at last ran along the sea's rim, reaching the west pier of Kingstown Harbour.

ON TO KINGSTOWN

We have already described some of the objectors to the Kingstown extension but once the proposed route of the railway line across the harbour became known others entered the fray.

The map by one of the D&KR's engineers (Fig. 3.7) clearly shows the path to be taken. On it we can see several important features that were central to the arguments of the objectors. These are the Old Harbour, the

Martello tower (marked Tower on map) and the Ordnance Battery.[10]

It is also obvious that the line took the most direct and coast-hugging path to the point near the yet-to-be-built New Wharf where the steam packets were to berth.

The company wished to build an embankment across the Old Harbour, cutting off a significant portion of it and creating yet another lagoon. There was to be another small embankment before the line reached the New Wharf. The Old Harbour was at this stage under the control of the Ballast Board (the precursor of the Dublin Port and Docks Board) and their Inspector of Works, George Halpin, objected most strongly to interference with the harbour. Plans by the Ballast Board were submitted to the Lords of the Admiralty who were, at this time, the *de jure* controllers of all the coast and seas of Ireland. These gentlemen laid down many restrictions and demands, one of which was that the D&KR should construct a 'compensation' harbour in recompense for the damage to the existing Old Harbour.

The D&KR company, in a memorial signed by William Cubitt and transmitted with a letter from James Pim to the Lords Commissioners

---

10   See J. Bolton et al, *The Martello Towers of Dublin,* Dún Laoghaire and Fingal Councils, 2012.

Fig. 3.7: The Kingstown extension (creator unknown).

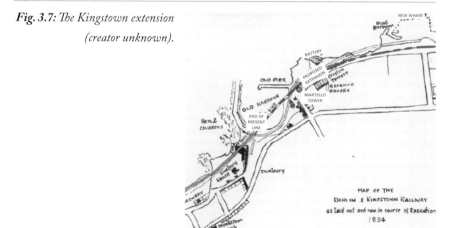

of the Office of the Lord High Admiral, agreed to build a compensation harbour and requested authorisation to proceed with the line and take the matter of the harbour later. They never did build the compensation harbour but had as an ally in their disobedience the then Lord Lieutenant, Earl Mulgrave, and his servants, the Commissioners of Public Works, and with these the Sea Lords would have had to pursue this matter of the compensation harbour. The Admiralty Lords baulked at the prospect of taking on people so powerful, so the compensation harbour never came into being. However, this caused considerable rancour: the Lords of the Treasury and the Admiralty long remembered the incident and the assertion that the Lord Lieutenant alone had sanction on public works in Ireland.[11] The issue of the this compensation harbour was to arise again in 1843 (see Chapter 6: 'Atmospheric to Dalkey').

Next was the matter of the Martello tower and the battery, operated and controlled by HM Board of Ordnance. The battery and its attendant Martello tower (South 13), one of fifty-seven that dotted the Irish coast, was constructed to help repel an invasion by Napoleonic forces.[12] After the defeat of Napoleon and the coming of peace after the Peninsular Wars the tower was disarmed in 1825 and given into the charge of the Water Guard (the precursors of the Coast Guard). The battery continued to be armed but, as the new harbour enfolded it, it was of little strategic value and there was already talk of creating a new battery at the end of the east pier.

Plans for the railway cutting, which included a buttress wall, were duly drawn up (see Fig. 3.8) but the Board of Ordnance initially insisted that the line come no nearer to the tower than 20 feet. The Ordnance then relented and for a payment of £1700 sold the tower and battery to the Commissioners of Public Works to allow the building of the railway

---

11   See House of Commons Papers, HC 265, Vol. 43, 1844.

12   The Martello tower stood at the end of present-day Clarence Street and Crofton Road, close to the base of the old pier, and had been built on the site of the old dún (fort) of King Laoire. The tower was one of a pair in Kingstown: the other stood on the site of People's Park. Both suffered the same fate. The South 13 battery was on the site of the Irish Lights building.

extension. The tower was quickly demolished.[13]

The Board of Ordnance wished to maintain the battery for some time. They insisted that a strong over-bridge be built across the railway to allow heavy ordnance to be brought to and from the battery. (I presume this was to replace an existing low ordnance bridge that crossed the tramway near the battery.) It is unclear how quickly the Martello tower and Battery No 13 were demolished, but the OS map of 1837 shows no sign of either structure.

The replacement bridge, most probably created with stonework from the tower, had an elegant elliptical arc and spanned both lines of the railway and the harbour tramway (of which more later). It was accompanied in 1854 by a triple-arch bridge built to accommodate new road construction. These old bridges stood until the electrification of the line in 1981, when the current rather unlovely one replaced them.

The way was now clear and on demolition of the Martello tower the line could proceed to the New Wharf. Can the construction of any

---

13   See J. Bolton et al, *The Martello Towers of Dublin.* Dún Laoghaire and Fingal Councils, 2012.

Fig. 3.8: *Proposed route of the line past the Martello tower (looking towards Dublin).*

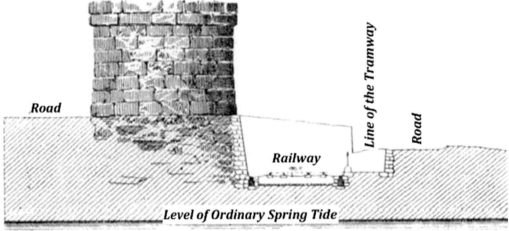

Fig. 3.9: Old Harbour embankment (c. 1900).

short section of line have ever given rise to such a range of protests and objections?

Dargan again took on the work, funded by yet another loan from the Board of Public Works, this time in the sum of £37,200. The embankments were built. They were walled and filled using material from Dalkey quarries (more later) and other available infill materials. Fig. 3.9 shows the embankment across the Old Harbour (Note the infill on the landward side. This again used material from Dalkey. When we look at the 1907 OSI map we see this infilled section occupied by a gasworks.) On 13 May 1837 the newspapers stated that the work was complete. At last the Dublin and Kingstown Railway had achieved its original goal!

Originally the line had only three stations; the two termini and Blackrock. Additional intermediate stations came and went and came back again over the history of this line as it changed hands. The original stations were the following:

Westland Row

The original terminus station house (Fig. 3.10) presented a simple and elegant façade on Westland Row. It was two storeyed, with three entrances to the booking offices and waiting rooms on the ground floor. A further entrance provided for cab access to the platforms. The façade was 91 feet

Fig. 3.10: The original façade of Westland Row station house (1834).

long. The passenger shed was on the level of the second floor and passengers approached from the booking office by convenient staircases (Fig. 3.11).

There were four rail lines under the shed; the arrival lines being separated from the departure lines by an iron railing. Drawbridges provided convenient passages from the platforms to the island platform ('P' in Fig. 3.11); these were readily lifted to permit the passage of a train.

Note also the separation of third-class passengers from those of second and first class. Not only did they ascend by different staircases, a rail was placed between the third class and the first and second class departure platforms. This in the words of the D&KR would 'allow the superior customers to come opposite their carriages without obstruction from their inferiors'.

There were several minor organisational and structural changes over the early years, and for a description of the more significant alterations which were made to the fabric of Westland Row station house over time see Chapter 7: 'Later Years'.

Kingstown Station

This is a more complex story as the line had first to terminate at the edge of the harbour near Salthill. This was at a point beyond the site of the

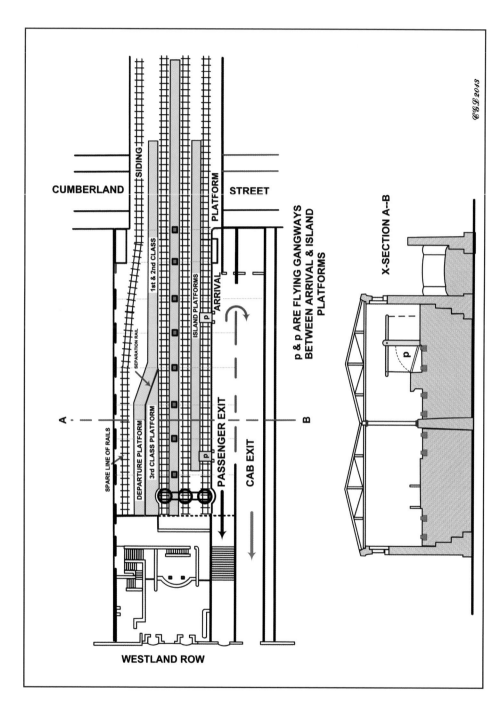

Fig. 3.11: *Plan of Westland Row station house c. 1835 (adapted from Grierson).*

present-day Purty Kitchen, where at that time stood the Dunleary Coffee House, a great haunt for Dubliners on a day at the sea.

Because the board of D&KR knew that in a short time permission would be given to extend the line to near the east pier they did not waste money on a grand structure, merely built a simple wooden shed to shelter the passengers. Mail was brought to the station by means of a cart attended by a guard. I can find no image of this structure, which was demolished in 1837.

Then, when the extension to Kingstown was complete, the board adapted some of the existing buildings on the site. A police barracks and stables were converted into a parcel office, a refreshment room and a house for the station superintendent. Plans for a new station finally gained approval in 1839 and Samuel Roberts won the contract to build it. The station, estimated at £650, was to be a fairly simple structure.

There was some squabbling and the D&KR board suspended the work. The company then decided that the station should be built at the end of the line rather than beside it. Instructions were given to the board's architect, J.S. Mulvany[14], who designed the building we all know

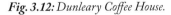

14. John Skipton Mulvany (1813-70) was a notable Irish architect and most of the buildings he designed are still in daily use. He was apprenticed to William Deane Butler, who was responsible for many fine classical courthouses and Gothic churches. Mulvany, an admirer of James Gandon, began by undertaking works for the D&KR and became their de facto architect. His best-known building is Broadstone Station and he also designed Kingstown Station, Galway Railway Station and

Fig. 3.12: Dunleary Coffee House.

Fig. 3.13: *Kingstown Station from the Pavilion gardens c. 1890, showing the over-cover of the atmospheric railway.*

(Fig. 3.13). Roberts took the contract for building, which was now costed at £2800. The base level was in a poor stone but the upper portion was Wicklow granite, which has stood the test of time.

The station had two platforms and sidings. There was a separate entrance/exit on the harbour side of the building and a hall with a domed glass roof. On the upper level were the booking office and other offices. The station also featured a large terrace surrounded by a balustrade.

After the addition of the functional DART offices on the side of the building the main structure was abandoned for rail purposes and is now a restaurant. The elegance of the building can still be enjoyed if one takes the right viewpoint.

BLACKROCK STATION

In 1834 Blackrock was a bustling little village of some three hundred houses and a population of about 2000. Originally the station was the only intermediate one serviced by the line. The first building was a little more to the east than the present structure. The existing building is another typical Mulvany design, undertaken in 1841-2. The 'up' platform has an over-canopy supported by cast-iron pillars. On the down side there was a

the terminus hotel, the clubhouse for the Royal Irish Yacht Club and, for William Dargan, Mount Anville House.

Fig. 3.14: Exterior (1970) and interior of Blackrock Station (showing the shelter c. 1870).

Mulvany-designed shelter (see Fig. 3.14), the roof of which was replaced by a glass and iron structure in 1895.

The D&KR also built a public baths beside the station with access via steps on the down platform. The creation of these baths was in part to make up for the loss of Blackrock strand, which was a popular bathing place until the construction of the railway closed off the shoreline.

The other negative effect of the embankment that closed the space between the shore and the railway was the creation of an area that flooded with sea water only at high tide. In warm weather this became a malodorous salty marsh similar to the one in Booterstown. This marsh was a cause of local inconvenience and displeasure for years until its owner, the Earl of Pembroke, donated it to Blackrock and Blackrock Town Commissioners (a body that had been established in 1860) took steps in the early 1870s to fill in the area and create a park. The park stretches from Blackrock to Booterstown and encompasses Williamstown.

STATION NAME	TYPE	OPENED	BUILT BY	CLOSURES AND REOPENINGS
Grand Canal Street	Railway works	1856	D&KR	Closed 1925: never reopened.
Lansdowne Road	Intermediate	1/7/1870	DW&WR	
Sandymount Lane (now Sandymount Avenue)	Intermediate	1835	D&KR	Closed 1841: reopened 01/08/1860. Closed 1/4/1862: reopened 1/2/1883. Closed 1/2/1902: reopened 1/4/1928. Closed 12/9/1960: reopened 23/7/1984.
Serpentine Avenue	Intermediate	1835	D&KR	Closed 02/4/1862: never reopened.
Sydney Parade	Intermediate	1835	D&KR	Closed 6/1841: reopened 1/10/1862. Closed 12/9/1960: reopened 6/6/1972.
Merrion	Intermediate	1835	D&KR	Closed 6/1862: reopened 1/10/1882. Closed 1/9/1935: never reopened.
Booterstown	Intermediate	1835	D&KR	
Williamstown	Intermediate	1/1835	D&KR	Closed 8/1841: never reopened.
Blackrock	Intermediate	1/7/1834	D&KR	
Seapoint	Intermediate	1/7/1862	DW&WR	
Salthill	Intermediate	5/1837	D&KR	Closed 02/4/1960: totally rebuilt and reopened 29/7/1984.

Table 3.1: *Details of intermediate stations along the line of the Dublin and Kingstown Railway.' Built' signifies a permanent station house or structure being put in place.*

INTERMEDIATE STATIONS

Apart from Blackrock Station there were six early stations that opened in 1835; three further stations opened between 1837 and 1870, although we must be careful about using the term 'station' for them. Some details of these are given in Table 3.1. In general, in the early years, they were little more than a pair of slightly raised gravel-covered embankments with access steps, one to each of the up and down lines of the railway. In 1837 somewhat more substantial platforms were built but some of these were no higher than 15-18 inches and initially of wood, which presented serious danger during wet or frosty conditions. Another serious danger was that passengers alighting from down trains and those who needed to take a down train had to walk across the tracks. Indeed people also put themselves in danger by using the tracks as a route to avoid the mud and dirt of Rock Road.

The complex coming and going of these stations was as a result of revenue increasing and decreasing and also due to pressure exerted by the commissioners of the Pembroke estate. This vast estate extended through south-east County Dublin, from Merrion Square along the coast through Merrion out to Blackrock, inland through Mount Merrion to Dundrum and beyond to the Dublin mountains. It was the largest family-owned estate in County Dublin, and an absolute goldmine as the city exploded southwards from the late 18th century onwards: cumulatively it was probably the most valuable estate in Ireland.

Pembroke township was formed for local government purposes by a private act of parliament in 1863. It was governed by commissioners until 1899, when it became an urban district, and in 1930 it was absorbed into the City and County Borough of Dublin.

The township consisted of a number of distinct areas, including Ringsend, which was an old fishing village, and Irishtown, an industrial district. The remainder comprised affluent residential areas. Seven-ninths of the township belonged to the Pembroke estate, and the agent of the estate was an ex-officio commissioner, the remaining fourteen being elected by property owners. Both the Earl of Pembroke and his estate had a great deal of influence on the D&KR with regard to the section of line that ran through its properties. The earl indulged in philanthropic donations and payments to improve areas, such as the gifting of the sea lagoon enclosed by the railway embankment in Blackrock to the Blackrock commissioners and moneys to develop this area into Blackrock Park as a 'place for proper entertainments of the lower orders and for gentlefolk…'

So we see that on opening the railway had three stations: the fine terminus at Westland Row, Blackrock Station and the wooden station at Old Dunleary Harbour. Passengers travelling on the rail experienced alarming speed and as the train left Merrion Gate the strange sensation of flying over water as they crossed the sea lagoons in Booterstown and Blackrock. All this must have created great excitement and made the journey a 'must-have' experience.

By 1835 there were seven intermediate stations on the line. The frequency of trains increased, as did the time span over which they operated. Trains now ran from Westland Row from 8.00am until 5.40pm and departed Kingstown from 9.00am until 7.00pm. Below is Pim's timetable:

Slow trains, well lighted, will start from Westland Row at seven o'clock pm and half past right o'clock; and from Kingstown at a quarter before eight o'clock and a quarter past nine and will stop at Blackrock only.

SHORT STAGES

The carriages which leave both ends of the line	will stop at
Nine o'clock forenoon	Booterstown and Williamstown
Twenty mins after nine	Blackrock and Merrion
Forty mins after nine	Booterstown and Sandymount Lane
Ten o'clock forenoon	Booterstown and Sidney Parade
Twenty mins after ten	Booterstown and Williamstown
Forty mins after ten	Blackrock and Merrion
& so forth to	
Forty mins after five	Blackrock and Merrion

Passengers for short stages are requested to go into the labelled carriages.
On Sundays the 'hour' trains will stop at Blackrock; no stop will be made on that day at any other intermediate stations…

The service, already good, expanded over the subsequent years, with the company dispatching some two thousand passengers within an hour on busy days.

Now to return to the creation of stations. D&KR created a station at Serpentine Avenue, but low revenue returns brought about its closure and replacement by Sandymount Lane (a simple halt, not a station). Again poor returns from Sandymount caused its demise and from early 1841

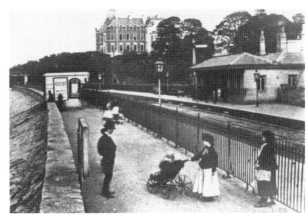

Fig. 3.15: Salthill Station and Salthill Hotel c. *1870.*

there were no regular stops between Westland Row and Booterstown.

After much pressure from various committees and interested parties D&KR agreed to reopen the station at Sandymount Lane but again revenue was poor and it was closed in 1862. Later that year the company reopened Sydney Parade, again after pressure from the Pembroke commissioners.

BOOTERSTOWN STATION

In 1834 Booterstown was already a prosperous little village with some fine houses and estates so a passage to the station was built in the form of an embankment (Map 2.1) from Rock Road to the railway and a small station house with space for hackney carriages was constructed.

The station did well.

WILLIAMSTOWN STATION

Williamstown was a village with a population of 356 and had pleaded for a station. One was provided by the D&KR (the OS map for 1837 shows no buildings) but it did not make money for the company so it was permanently closed in 1841 A pedestrian way to the strand was provided, allowing bait-diggers and bathers access the beach and to the baths.

This completed the number of stations until the railway was extended to the Royal Harbour in Kingstown in 1837.

SALTHILL STATION

With the closing and removal of the wooden station at the Old Harbour there was a long run back to Blackrock, so the decision was made to create a station in Salthill. The name Salthill denoted salt-works on the site; indeed the position of the station is where a mineral water plant operated. The station made sense as the company came to own a nearby hotel, The Salthill, and also had its main baths on the strand. A neat Swiss-cottage style station house was built (Fig. 3.15). A footbridge from the hotel gave access to the baths situated on the foreshore (where the pumping station on the west pier is now). This, the second iron and masonry footbridge on the line, was of a novel design, with an iron spiral staircase on a cylindrical pillar (Fig. 3.17). The ironwork was demolished to assist the electrification of the line but its masonry towers survive.

Now we move forward to 1862, at the time when the Dublin, Wicklow and Wexford Railway (DW&WR) was in control of the line. It was at this time or after this date that the final stations on the line were created.

SEAPOINT STATION

After much pressure by Seapoint residents it was agreed to provide a station and a station house was built. There were two reasons for the rather strange design of this building: space inland was very limited and horse stabling had to be provided to replace existing stables lost by the construction. This accounts for its circular windows (contrary to many arguments it was never a locomotive shed). The station, unexpectedly, performed very well and became permanent.

LANSDOWNE STATION

With the demise of Haig's Distillery (Map 3.1) and other changes in its vicinity the Pembroke estate put considerable effort into developing the surrounding area into one of high-class residences. As part of this campaign Haig's Lane was gentrified as Lansdowne Road. In 1869 the estate came to an agreement with the DW&WR to develop a station at the junction of the road and the railway, with the estate and DW&WR sharing the cost and the D&KR having a buy-out right should the station prove successful. It was successful and D&KR did buy it out. Over time, as the local population grew and the station did well, stone platforms, shelters and a brick building were added.

MERRION STATION

Table 3.1 indicates the closure in 1862 of the 'halt' at Merrion Gates. The station had been maintained up to this date and had even had its platforms lengthened and improved, even though business was poor. Strangely, it was maintained as an active station even though agreement on its closure had been reached with the Pembroke estate. However the DW&WR decided on its closure and it remained closed until 1882, when the DW&WR made the decision to reactivate it and construct the fine little red-brick station on the down line.[15] After a number of years in which the receipts were, again, disappointing, the station closed permanently in 1935.

This completes the account of the stations of the line until the coming of the DART.

The D&KR had other important buildings:

THE GRAND CANAL WORKS

Initially the locomotives were serviced in the 'engine hospital' in Serpentine Road. As far as I can divine this small building was closer to Sandymount Lane than Serpentine and, I believe, across the line from the Railway Cottages. This facility soon became too small for purpose, so other premises were needed. It seemed sensible that they should be

---

15 The station house is currently used by the Simon Community as a refuge for homeless men.

near the Westland Row terminus, but space was difficult to create. Then a strange proposition was made by an ad hoc grouping of the principal Dublin distillers: they offered an inducement of £1000 if the D&KR would purchase the Dock Distillery at Grand Canal Dock. This was closed because of the lack of success of the distilling business and the financial difficulties of Aeneas Coffey (1780-1852), the inventor of the pot still. In 1836 the D&KR took possession of the site for £5500 minus the £1000 inducement. The company duly moved in and modified the premises, which contained a useful stationary steam engine. The conversion work was done by Courtney and Stephens and the ironwork firm J. & R. Mallet and in 1839 all locomotive business in Serpentine Road ceased and moved to Grand Canal Dock.

One of the benefits of having the Grand Canal site (Map 3.1) was that Coffey had created a reservoir at the distillery, so a water tank was installed on the roof of the main building. This gave sufficient head height to deliver water to the locomotives in Westland Row, saving them from having to make the run to the Grand Canal to take on water.

Although a building conceived as a distillery does not necessarily make a good engine and coachworks this venture was a success. Engine frames and boilers were 'bought in' in a semi-finished state, but aside from this all other locomotive manufacturing was completed at the Grand Canal Works.

The early engines required a lot of maintenance for minor repairs and overhauling so there was a crew for each engine. The service bays in the works were served from a siding and turntables (see Map 3.1). Strangely, locomotive service was carried out on the first floor and engines had to be raised to this level for service and lowered when service was completed.

From the day the works opened all carriage work was completed there and it continued in use after the lease of the D&KR by DW&WR and its final takeover by the Dublin and South Eastern Railway (DSER). As it developed it came to include a foundry, a boiler shop, a smithy and engine room, a punching and sawing shop, a copper shop, a fitting shop and a pattern room. The company also provided houses for the works superintendent and the foreman: these are clearly shown on the OS map of 1907.

THE SALTHILL HOTEL

As the D&KR believed it would soon get royal assent for extension of the line to Kingstown Harbour it decided that in order to have no sharp curves in the line it would go past Salthill House on the seaward side rather than making the considerable landward deviation necessary to avoid the hill on which it stood. This required taking over some of the Salthill's gardens and to achieve their goal they were obliged to buy both grounds and house. When the clay cliff to the sea was cut away they had a straight run across to the old harbour of Dunleary.

William Dargan rented the house from D&KR for the duration of the construction of the line and when the project was completed the company created pleasure gardens (the Longford Gardens) at the foot of the house and turned the house into an hotel. The gardens were used for flower shows and other 'polite amusements suitable for gentlefolk'. The company itself never operated the hotel but leased it to a number of individuals, such as William Marsh at £250 per annum and the Lovegroves. In 1842 the hotel was sold and again a number of proprietors leased it. Some fine

Fig. 3.16: Blackrock Baths c. 1900, also showing the footbridge and signal pole.

Fig. 3.17: Images of Salthill Hotel showing the footbridge and the by then derelict baths.

chefs worked there: for instance, Paul Bessler, a German gourmet chef of considerable reputation, was proprietor in 1911.

The hotel continued in business until it was badly damaged by fire in 1970. The building then lay derelict until it was demolished in 1972 and eventually the Salthill apartment complex was built within the hotel's grounds. In the enclosing wall of the garden of the complex can still be seen the old main gateway marked 'Salthill' and another sign showing 'To the Railway'.

THE BATHS

One of the things Charles Blacker Vignoles noticed when he walked the route of the proposed line were the numbers of sea bathers, both male and female. His memoirs note: '…there seems to be a positive mania among the local populace for sea bathing.'

The cutting off of the foreshore by the railway embankments meant that many of the existing bathing places (such as the Peafield Baths in Blackrock) were contained within the lagoons created. As water quality in these areas was spoiled they became unusable. This created a great deal of annoyance and protest.

To placate bathers the D&KR created a number of ways to the

beach and swimming slipways at points along the line. They also decided to build two cold sea-water baths, one in Blackrock, the other in Salthill.

Blackrock Baths, completed in 1839, included two sets of steps and slips for the segregated sexes. Each tide renewed the water and swimming depth was good, in general. The baths also had segregated shelters for dressing and undressing. Salthill Baths were more elaborate, sporting two fine stone-lined pools, the larger one for males and the smaller for ladies. Each pool had its own bathing boxes and a high 'modesty' wall ensured the privacy that was expected in this era. Every tide renewed the water and swimming depth was always good. Hot baths and shower facilities were available and altogether it was an up-to-date and rather posh establishment. There was ready access to the baths from a path alongside the railway and also via a footbridge from the Salthill Hotel. (see Fig. 3.17).

The opening in 1843 of the very elegant Victoria Baths in Kingstown caused the decline of the Salthill Baths and they were abandoned in about 1870 after a number of years of decline. Their sorry fate was to become a dumping ground and eventually part of the reclaimed land where the west pier pumping station is located.

CHAPTER 4

THE RAILS

Longitudinal and Transverse Sleepers

When the D&KR began its operations there was no standard gauge for railways; neither was there a standard form of rail profile or specific weight for rails. Vignoles seems to have been in favour of a broad gauge but as the engines bought from Britain were made to what was known as 'Stephenson's gauge', a rail spacing of 4 feet 8½ inches had to be adopted. The method of laying rails at this period must also be considered to have been experimental: Vignoles adopted the practice of using stone sleepers with the rails held by 'chairs' which were pinned to the sleepers, the abutting sections of rail being held in a special chair. This was the method used by the Stockton and Darlington Railway (S&DR), the first in the UK. Robert Stephenson (1803-59), its engineer, put forward the design that sleeper blocks should be set with their diagonals perpendicular to the rails (see Fig. 4.1). This, he believed, made it easier for the navvies laying the rails to have better access to all the faces of a sleeper block.

However, on the S&DR sleepers were set square to the run of the rails. They were laid with a 'running' pitch of 3 feet, as were the D&KR blocks. Following the practice on S&DR Vignoles oriented the sleepers 'square on' to the rails; I cannot determine his reasoning for doing this rather than taking the 'diagonal' approach.

The stone sleepers were 2 feet 3 inches square and a foot thick and

Fig. 4.1: *The rail and sleeper system of the early railways (after Simmons).*

often of granite, as were the D&KR sleepers. The setting of the sleepers on which the rails rest is obviously a matter of great importance as it determines the stability of the iron road. The method used, after having established the embankment or way, was to lay small gravel or ashes (ballast) on which to bed the sleepers. The sleepers, or 'blocks', with the chairs and rails already attached, were placed on the ballast by the navvies, who lifted and dropped the assembly several times to bed it in. It was levelled by extracting or pushing in extra sand or ashes under the sleeper blocks while beating on the rails with heavy mallets. This was exhausting and slow work with very little rail set down per day.

Frederick Williams, an early historian of the railway, reports:

> Further the seating or solidity of the rails was no more than was given
> by the blows of the mallets on the blocks which having little effect
> in compressing or consolidating the foundation, when the carriages
> came to run upon the rails the blocks sunk down and it required
> workmen to be constantly pushing ashes or sand underneath them,
> to raise them to their proper level, until they came to a permanent
> seat; or, in fact till the seats of the blocks became sufficiently firm to
> resist the weight of the carriages weight passing over them.[1]

1   Frederick S. Williams, *Our Iron Rails: their History, Construction and Influences,* London:

This method does not sound very satisfactory and was bound to give trouble when teamed with a recently laid embankment. Obviously for this plan to succeed it was essential that the material on which ballast coating was set should be perfectly firm and solid; so the system worked only on well-drained ground or heavily compacted embankments. Various tricks were resorted to, one being the use of a 'diagonal set' for the sleeper blocks, believed to give greater stability.

Vignoles added some further variants to the practice by using sleepers of differing sizes, along with a cross sleeper with the dimensions of 7x2½x1 foot every fifth yard. This 'through going block' was to preserve the gauge of the rails. The differing sizes also allowed the construction of rail switches or sidings (see Fig. 4.2).

Under the direction of Vignoles, Dargan used a ballast of 'very coarse gravel or shingle' topped by a layer of Killiney sand or fine gravel. The 'boxing' or over-cover of the ballast was of clean sand or gravel put in 3-inch layers and well but gently punned by light rammers. Two inches of gravel were laid over this, with a slight fall to the sides and centres, the whole being beaten down so that it was flush with the top of the blocks, then grouted with a thin layer of washed lime.

Vignoles used a T-rail with a button top and square flat bottom (weighing 45 lbs per yard) mounted in chairs that were fixed to the sleepers by two iron pins hammered into oak plugs 1 inch in diameter in

Ingrams Cooke and Company, 1852.

Fig. 4.2: Granite sleepers accommodating crossing rails.

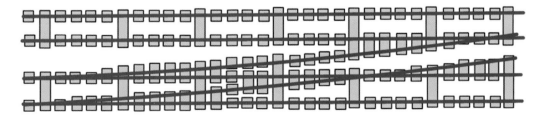

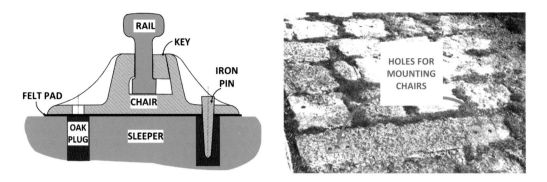

Fig. 4.3: A D&KR rail chair assembly and granite sleepers, drilled for chair mounting.

each sleeper (see Fig. 4.3). These sleepers were subsequently used to form sections of the pathways along the embankments and can still be seen in places along the line.

Fig. 4.3 shows the rail to be locked in the chair by means of a key. At this time keys such as this were generally of thoroughly seasoned oak or beech and were about 9 inches long. In order to give the whole great firmness keys were steamed and then subjected to a pressure of 12 lbs per square inch (50kPa) by a hydraulic machine, which of course greatly reduced their dimensions. Keys were then stored in a drying house until required. The keys were fitted into the chair by hammering and so locked the rail tightly in place. Because of their relatively short life wooden keys were eventually replaced by iron ones. Whishaw writes that the keys employed by the D&KR were wooden; however, Thomas Grierson makes it quite clear that the line used wrought-iron keys from the start.

The chairs used on the D&KR were of cast iron and weighed 16 lbs with those under rail joints weighing 20½ lbs. Felt pads were placed under each chair as it was pinned to a sleeper. John Bradley and Company of Stourbridge, Worcester, made the chairs and rails and, according to Grierson, the pins and keys.

The granite sleepers needed for the line (some 40,000) were Irish-made, cut, shaped and drilled by Dargan's workers. This was a slow and laborious task and production levels were impossible to maintain: coupled with the tedious method of settling and laying the rails it meant that it would not be possible for Dargan to meet the deadline for opening the railway.

Vignoles, worried about the delays, suggested an alternative approach. His solution was to use sleepers made of wood and this was done for a considerable length of line (towards Salthill). Although this was a change made in desperation it was a most fortunate one as the concept of an entirely rigid railway line was completely wrong-headed. Vignoles should not be made to take all the blame for this idea as it was the popular theory of the time. A considerable length of stone-sleepered rigid line was laid, something that had serious consequences for the D&KR.

Dargan stopped using granite block and began the task of laying the remainder of the track with wooden sleepers so that the track was duly completed by mid-October.

Even in the earliest days of the D&KR springs and axles needed to be replaced because of the shock loads from the rails. After two years of operation and despite constant attention to maintenance the condition of the rails was bad. The pounding caused by the engines bent the rails between their supports and when a block sank its key, the pins, the chair or the rail had to break. This made for serious damage to the engines and carriages. Results from the section of line with wooden sleepers were much more encouraging, so Vignoles began a series of experiments. He tried a number of different materials as shock absorbers under the chairs but none provided any improvement, all eventually becoming compacted and losing their elastic properties.

Then Vignoles had a section of the granite block line near Grand Canal Dock lifted and replaced with longitudinal sleepers. Rail was still set in chairs but rail supports or saddles were added between them (see Fig. 4.4). The gauge was maintained by fitting cross-members between the sleepers. In eighteen months of service this section gave no trouble.

Vignoles borrowed this method from the standard practice on Brunel's Great Western Railway (GWR).

By 1837, almost all the chairs were loose on the stone-laid section of the line and thousands of keys were out of place. As the damage to engines and carriages was so serious, something needed to be done – and done quickly. In June of that year Vignoles expressed his dismay at this state of affairs in his report to the directors of D&KR: '…the cause of the breakage of the rails and the heavy shocks resulting daily to the engines and carriages on most parts of the line was the fruitless attempt to obtain a perfectly rigid railway.' He continued:

This error I have to lament in common with many other engineers, few of whom are yet convinced…the proximate cause is partly from the play the rail sustains throughout its whole length, by the action of the chair and block, or either of them. If the chair remains fast to the block, the latter is lifted and hangs on the rails, and ultimately is rammed until its bed is too low to allow the block to take any bearing and finally the heads of the chair pins are jerked off. If the chair is loosened, the same effect takes place, and adds to the continued rattle and wear and tear of the line.

He added: 'The best remedy is the simple one of laying the whole line upon "kyanised"[2] longitudinal timber and placing between each chair

2   John Howard Kyan (1774-1850) invented the 'kyanising' process for preserving wood, which he patented in 1832. He extended the application to the preservation of paper, canvas and cordage and was granted a further patent in 1836. The process consisted in the submersion of timber or other materials in a tank containing a solution of bichloride of mercury in water. Kyan maintained that permanent chemical combination took place between the mercurial salt and the woody fibre, but this was contested. It became evident that iron fastenings could not be used in wood treated with sublimate because of the corrosive action of the sublimate. The salt was somewhat expensive and other methods of preserving, by chloride of zinc and later by creosote, provided strong competition. Doubts began to be expressed as to the real efficiency of kyanising and the process gradually ceased to be employed. One thinks also of the health hazards involved in this process.

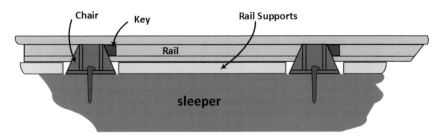

Fig. 4.4: Chaired rail with supports.

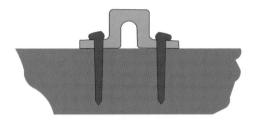

Fig. 4.5: Cross-section of bridge rail pinned to sleepers.

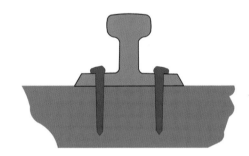

Fig. 4.6: Cross-section of Vignoles flanged rail.

an iron-bearing piece.'[3]

Now that the advantages of wooden sleepers had become so obvious, a restoration of the line began: as Vignoles had proposed, longitudinal kyanised wooden sleepers with bridge rails (see Fig. 4.5) held in chairs were used on some sections. This followed the practice of the GWR.

However, this rail form was not adopted permanently. Vignoles knew the shape of rail he wanted (the Vignoles-Stevens rail) which could be held directly on the wooden sleeper by means of iron spikes, so dispensing with chairs (Fig. 4.6). However, he seems not to have forcefully

3   Olinthus J. Vignoles, *Life of Charles Blacker Vignoles, Soldier and Civil Engineer: A Reminiscence of Early Railway History*, London and New York: Longman Greene and Company, 1889.

advanced his ideas to the board at this stage.

On the other hand Murray[4] states that during the restoration of the line some parts of the track had Vignoles rail section laid on them and he went on to have other railways under his control laid with this form of rail.

In 1839 Vignoles wrote:

Every day's experience convinces me of the propriety of laying the rails altogether on baulks of wood placed longitudinally and by rolling a rail of 50 lbs weight in the annexed form (the Vignoles rail) I dispense with the use of chairs and obtain a better fastening, simple and less expensive. It would cost £1000 less/mile than one with stone blocks and repairs would be cheaper. Great savings would accrue in diminished wear and tear, not only to the railway but also to the engines and carriages passing over it from the smoothness and absence of vibrations. After my eighteen months with the D&KR I am more and more convinced.

With improved ballast being used the replacement of rail on the D&KR followed. Murray states that the final rail was 'double head', weighing some 5 lbs per yard more than previously used rails. He does not clarify whether this was on longitudinal or transverse sleepers.

In 1839 Whishaw stated that by the autumn of that year:

...one line of the way had been laid with longitudinal sleepers, and the other with transverse timbers...the transverse sleepers are 6 feet long laid and measure 7 inches by 13 inches. The chairs are fixed to the transverse sleepers with 10-inch spikes. The rails are in no case with continuous bearings but are fixed in chairs, and rest on intermediate saddles.[5]

---

4   K.A. Murray, *Ireland's First Railway*, Dublin: IRRS, 1981.

5   There is no dichotomy between the statements of Murray and Whishaw but there is lack

Fig. 4.7: *Vignoles flat-bottomed rail held with Pandrol clips.*

So it seems Vignoles did not get his way on the D&KR, even though as consulting engineer to the London and Croydon and the Cheltenham and Bromsgrove railways he ensured the installation of the Vignoles-type rail on these lines. Time has shown Vignoles was correct in his considerations. Much of the world's rail track is now of the flanged type. The rail's profile and other geometric and physical properties are specified in International Standards BS EN 13674-1: 2011.

In 1959 Per Pande Rolfson developed the Pandrol clip, which tightens under vibration, so preventing the problem of trains dragging the track along when the brakes are applied. This innovation saves a lot of time and effort and the clips can be hammered in by man or machine. Pandrol clips are now the standard rail fixing throughout Europe and in many other parts of the world.

Over-bridges and Footbridges

The 1837 OSI maps show eight bridges over the railway. These, in sequence from Westland Row are:

Type of Bridge	Location
Wooden footbridge	Near foot of Bath Place (to gentlemen's bathing place)
Cloncurry's tower and bridge	Maretimo
Wooden footbridge	Via a gate beside 20 Maretimo Terrace to foreshore (on the estate of Harcourt Lee)

of clarity that requires much further research.

Wooden footbridge	From Seapoint House to a boat slip
Wooden footbridge	Almost colinear with Belgrave Road to baths on foreshore
Seapoint ordnance bridge	Seapoint Avenue to Martello tower

In 1878, when the line was under the control of DW&WR, the wooden footbridges were replaced by iron ones manufactured by Courtney Stephens and Bailey of Dublin. A number sufficient to instal footbridges in Lansdowne Road, Sidney Parade, Blackrock, Seapoint and Salthill stations were supplied. Fig. 3.13 shows one of the iron bridges and also a signal pillar.

LEVEL CROSSINGS

There were five significant roads that crossed the line where it ran at low level before reaching the coast. They had level crossings (called gates on the 1837 OSI map), manned gates that were held shut against the road traffic and open in favour of the trains. These were Lansdowne Road, Serpentine Avenue, Sandymount Lane, Sydney Gate and Merrion Gate. The extension of the railway across the Old Dunleary harbour to Kingstown necessitated a further crossing to give access to the west pier: this no longer exists.

SIGNALLING

As with other railways of the time no fixed signal methods were in use at the beginning of the D&KR's operations. A primary purpose of signals on the railway is to prevent collision between trains and with this in mind the D&KR established the rule that:

Every train on the railway shall after dusk show two red lights on the last carriage, and a green light from the foremost part of the train. Each gatekeeper and policeman[6] will also be provided with a red light to be exhibited when necessary. When the engineman,

6   These policemen were D&KR employees, 'of superior type', employed to watch over and walk the rails between stations.

fireman, or other person on the look-out shall perceive a single red light, the engineman shall slacken speed and stop at the light, and when a double red light is perceived the engineman shall not under any circumstances approach nearer than fifty yards.

A further rule decreed:

In every case wherein a train shall stop, whether from an accident occurring, or at any station for the purposes of taking up or setting down passengers, or in foggy weather, the policeman nearest at the time shall run at least 300 yards, or as far as may be necessary, behind said train, in order if needful to warn the engineman of the next coming train.

In addition to this the line was gaslit at nightfall. The lamps were supplied with town gas by the Hibernian Gas Company, which laid a gas line along the railway. They were lit, extinguished and maintained by D&KR workers and were much appreciated by one William Makepeace Thackeray, who

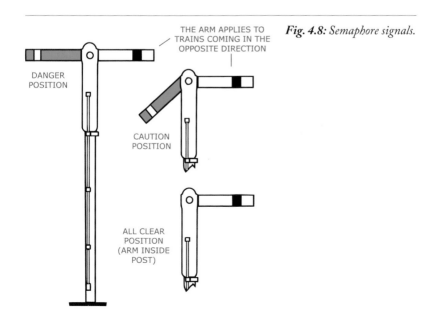

THE ARM APPLIES TO
TRAINS COMING IN THE
OPPOSITE DIRECTION

Fig. 4.8: Semaphore signals.

DANGER
POSITION

CAUTION
POSITION

ALL CLEAR
POSITION
(ARM INSIDE
POST)

viewed them from the windows of the Salthill Hotel as he waited for his hot lobster. However, the enginemen found them blinding as they proceeded along the line so instead of being a safety measure assisting in visual signals to the engine drivers they were a hazard and removed from service other than at level crossings and stations. Some of the lamps were modified by adding a vertical pole, on top of which was a large disc and at the bottom a handle for turning. This disc was oriented to show its face or its edge to the train to indicate a safe or unsafe transit. They were of the same type as used on the Liverpool and Manchester and Croydon railways.

In 1861, under the DW&WR, semaphore signals (see Fig. 4.8) replaced the gaslight system of the D&KR. These were on a tall pole midway on one platform and had two arms, one for up trains and one for down trains. The signals had three positions: Clear, Caution and Stop. For each direction there was an 'auxiliary' or 'distant' signal, worked by means of a wheel by the signalman. But as there was no interlocking between the station signal and the distant one, they could be unreliable. The enginemen complained when a negligent signalman failed to set the signal correctly and they had to make an emergency stop. We should remember that the brakes on these early trains were quite primitive and stopping required considerable skill on the part of the enginemen. In the mid-1860s interlocking between signals was installed at danger points such as the single line approach into Westland Row and the junction of the Carlisle Pier.

By 1925 signalling on the D&KR section of the now Dublin and South Eastern Railway (D&SER) line was controlled by signal cabins in Westland Row, Grand Canal Street, all the intermediate stations, Merrion Gates, Blackrock, Dún Laoghaire west pier crossing, Dún Laoghaire north and south boxes and Carlisle Pier, Sandycove and Dalkey.

From 1936, all signal systems were replaced by automatic track-controlled electric circuit signalling.

CHAPTER 5

THE EARLY LOCOMOTIVES AND ROLLING STOCK

Innovation and Class Distinction

The initial lot of six locomotives were all 2-2-0: two leading wheels on one axle, two powered driving wheels on one axle, and no trailing wheels. Three locomotives were manufactured by George Forrester and Company in the Vauxhall Foundry Liverpool; the others by Sharp, Roberts and Company, an establishment founded in 1828 and based in the Atlas Works, Great Bridgewater Street, Manchester. Forrester ceased locomotive building around 1847 and the company closed in 1890.

The Forrester locomotives, named *Dublin*, *Kingstown* and *Vauxhall* (see Appendix I),were highly innovative. For the first time horizontal cylinders were mounted at the front of the locomotive, outside the frame. Another innovation was that they employed four fixed eccentrics, rather than two loose ones, to operate the valve gear. A single linkage operated the whole arrangement at once, rather than the driver having four to operate, and the handles no longer rocked to and fro while the locomotive was in motion. These engines were extremely successful for their time. However, the outside cylinders and cranks caused the locomotives to sway so much that they were referred to as 'boxers' and they produced a giddying effect on the plate crew. To cure this problem an extra trailing axle was added to some of the locomotives supplied to the Liverpool and Manchester Railway.

In 1834 the Horsley Iron Company, Yorkshire, manufacturers of iron steam boats and bridges, supplied to D&KR the engine *Star*, which had been rejected by the board of the London and Manchester Railway Company and which Bergin had bought while in England. It was a disastrous purchase and after a series of failures and derailments caused by mechanical failure the board of D&KR decided to write the engine off.

In 1836 two further engines were supplied by Forrester, named *Comet* and *Victoria*. They carried their own fuel (coke) and water on their

Fig. 5.1: The Sharp, Roberts locomotive Experiment

CGC 2014

own frames and were the first ever tank engines in service on a passenger railway. All these engines did good work. The locomotive *Dublin* had a complete overhaul in 1839 and became a tank engine and by 1841 all the Forrester engines had been converted to tank engines. *Kingstown* had very few recorded repairs but was sold in 1846.

The technical details of these bought-in engines were as follows:

	SHARP, ROBERTS & COMPANY	FORRESTER & COMPANY
CONFIGURATION	2-2-0	2-2-0
GAUGE	4 feet 8 1/2 inches (1435 mm)	4 feet 8 1/2 inches (1435 mm)
LEAD WHEEL	3 feet (0.91 m)	3 feet (0.91 m)
DRIVER DIAMETER	5 feet (1.52 m)	4 feet 8½ inches (1.44 m)
BOILER PRESSURE	75 lbf/in² (517 kPa)	50 lbf/in² (345 kPa)
CYLINDERS	Two (vertical)	Two (horizontal)
CYLINDER SIZE	11 × 16 inches (28 × 41 cm)	11 × 16 inches (28 × 41 cm)
	TENDERS	
FUEL CARRIED	Coke (1 ton)	Coke
WATER CARRIED	600 gallons	?

The first locomotive constructed by Sharps, Roberts was for the Liverpool and Manchester Railway, a 2-2-0 called *Experiment*; it was withdrawn from use after a few months. The D&KR had three similar locomotives (*Hibernia*, *Britannia* and *Manchester*) constructed. These engines drove the wheels via a bell crank and suffered serious steam leakage from the vertical cylinders.

These locomotives also had piston valves, probably the reason the design was not a success, rather than the bell crank transmission, which was used successfully in other locomotives. Also the pounding, or 'churning' as the enginemen called it, caused by the vertical cylinders, did great damage to the engines, axles and springs and to the track, often causing rail fracture and subsidence. The engines were not a great success. In 1842, after it had been left unattended for a short period, the firebox of *Hibernia* blew up. The engine was scrapped and her two sisters were withdrawn from service and sold off, *Britannia* in 1843, *Manchester* in 1846.

Coke for these early locomotives was bought from the Dublin Gas Works at 17 shillings per ton. It was thought inferior to Worsley coke and believed to be 5 per cent less efficient thermodynamically.

The wheels of these engines were of cast iron with riveted-on wrought-iron tyres. The boilers were also of cast iron, their inner boxes of copper with boiler tubes of brass (bought as plate and rolled, formed and brazed).

For the guarantee period of a year these engines were cared for and driven by workmen sent by their manufacturers. They were tended in the engine hospital which lay in a siding in Serpentine Avenue.[1] The work of these men was shadowed by Irish workers with a view to having local operators and service for the D&KR. In the words of James Pim: 'the enginemen attending the carriages of the Kingstown Railway are English, but the company are training others, natives, to succeed them, with a certainty of success.'[2]

With all the experience gained on the nine bought-in engines, the engineering staff of the D&KR were in a good position to begin construction of their own engines, and in 1841 the *Princess*, named after the young Victoria, was the first locomotive to be built in Ireland (see Fig. 5.2): thus the D&KR became the first railway company in the world to manufacture its own locos.

The *Princess*, which was built at a cost of £1050/14s/5d, owed much to the design of the Forrester engines. Although the D&KR board had requested that some of the parts of the dismantled *Star* be used she was

---

1 I cannot positively identify the location of this building. The 1837 map shows no identifiable sidings but does state Old Engine House, without showing any footprint. This is located near the line of a siding which was built for the Royal Dublin Society and called the RDS Branch Railway. This line came into service in 1893. It ran to the far side of the Merrion Road from the RDS main building and to a point opposite its principal entrance. The branch line is clearly visible on the 1907 OS map. I assume the first section of this siding fed into the engine hospital.

2 Quoted in *The Dublin Penny Journal*, Vol. 14, No. 182, Dec 26 1835, pp. 203-5.

in fact all new. The engineer responsible for her construction was one Richard Pim: he and his apprentice, Samuel Haughton, were members of the Society of Friends. The number of Friends associated with the D&KR caused these Irish-made locomotives to be known as the 'Quaker engines'.

On 3 April 1841 *Princess* drew the train that carried the Lord Lieutenant, Earl de Grey, to Kingstown, a strong vote of confidence in a new engine. From 9 April she was in regular service.

Irish engine building continued, with *Bellisle* coming into service a short time after *Princess*. This used some parts of the ill-fated *Star*, so cost less than *Princess*. Locomotive manufacturing continued at the Grand Canal Works for many years, the last built by the D&KR being of the Burgoyne class (named in honour of Sir John Fox Burgoyne of the Commission of Public Works). The locomotive *Burgoyne* was the first of its class to be built, followed by *Cyclops*, *Vulcan* and *Jupiter*, which rolled out of the Grand Canal Works in 1847-8.

PASSENGERS AND FREIGHT

The carriages of each class, 1st, 2nd and 3rd, were superior to those in operation on the Stockton and Darlington and the Liverpool and Manchester Railway in that they were all covered; indeed even the freight

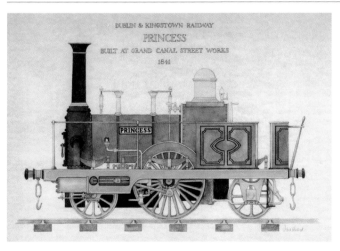

Fig. 5.2: *The D&KR-built locomotive* Princess.

carriages were covered. The early carriages were made by Dublin carriage makers with the sub-frame, wheels and axles coming from Britain.

Although the company decreed that 'the lower orders would not be rained upon', the third-class carriages had no doors or side covering above waist level. They did, however, have full height ends. Their layout was three large compartments and one small one, giving a total of seven seats with five passengers per seat sitting on bare timber with low backrests. The gross weight of a third-class carriage, including wheels, was 2 ton 15 cwt.

The second-class carriages, described by Whishaw in 1839 as being 'very much superior to any on other British railway services', were either 'open', without windows, or 'closed' that is, glazed. All had carpeted floors and some padding on the seats. As well as the glass in the door of the closed carriages there were six square side-lights on each side of the carriage. The seating arrangement in the second-class carriages was four passengers per seat with three compartments in the closed and an additional 'half compartment' in the open, giving capacities of twenty-four passengers and twenty-eight passengers in the latter. The total weight of each carriage was 3 ton 5 cwt.[3]

The first-class carriages for the higher orders were elegantly appointed, with a pair of comfortable cushioned seats – by 1839 spring-padded – with only three passengers per seat. The windows had blinds. There were three sub-carriages on each frame, giving a capacity of eighteen in first class. Each carriage weighed about 4 tons and cost £385.

The first class also had oil lamps for after dark but the second class had to wait till 1846 for this innovation. The third class went without light, but in 1840 canvas blinds were supplied on the seaward side.

Luggage was in a separate carriage called a luggage-truck or lorry, which was 12 feet long and weighed about 1½ ton. The mails were carried in a special form of luggage truck 15 feet in length and with on opening on each side fastened by an iron bar. The mail trucks had an attendant guard.

---

3   1 ton = 20 cwt; 1 cwt= 58 kg.

Each carriage had small steps (see Fig. 5.3a) which allowed passengers to alight at the intermediate stations – in the early these were little more than slightly raised embankments. These steps were soon replaced by pairs of footboards 10 inches wide to lessen the risk to passengers getting in and out. Health and safety were obviously not a major concern at this time.

One most significant addition to these carriages was Thomas Bergin's patented spring buffer (see Appendix II). This was specifically designed to preventing or lessen the concussions to railway carriages upon stopping or starting and was a great improvement on the overly-complex method adopted by the L&MR, which had a tendency to derail carriages. Mr Bergin claimed that this invention gave a perfectly steady motion to the trains to which it was applied. His buffer system also saved weight and the adapted frames were cheaper to make.

The early frames were made either by Sharp, Roberts or by Galloway of Glasgow: the Galloway frames were lighter. The technical details of these frames are shown in Table 5.1.

Frames, wheels and other components were supplied to Dublin firms of carriage makers, who completed their assembly into carriages.

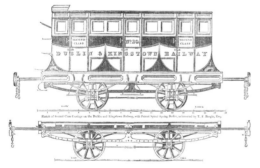

Fig. 5.3 (a): A D&KR closed second-class carriage showing Bergin's buffer.

Fig. 5.3 (b): A third-class carriage.

Frame size	17 feet long x 6 feet 1½inches wide (5.2 x 1.87 m)
Frame side beams manufactured	³⁄₁₆ x 9 inch deep iron face-plates with ends folded over for 9 inches. These were riveted to wood (ash or oak) inside.
Frame end beams	Wooden buffer beams of ash, 6 feet 1¼ inch long x 3 inches thick x 15 inches deep at mid and 9 inches at ends. They were covered by iron plate which was returned along the ends for 12 inches.
Wheels	4-inch x 3 feet 9-spoke cast-iron wrought-iron tyres.
Axles	Malleable cast iron. Their journal bearings were case-hardened. The wheels were held in place by a gib key and oil boxes fitted.

Table 5.1: Technical specifications of the early carriages.

Dawson of Capel Street made five first-class and ten second-class carriages. Courtney and Stephens of Blackhall Place principally made third-class carriages and a small number were completed in Manchester.

Dublin was renowned for its carriage makers and the quality of finish they supplied; so we can assume the livery of the carriages was handsome. The company intelligently decided to issue tickets of a different colour for each class of passenger and the livery of each class of carriage was the same colour as the ticket. (This obviated any possible occasions of embarrassment for the illiterate.) The livery colours were 'rich purple lake' for first class, pale yellow for second class closed and green for second class open. The third-class carriages were painted Prussian blue. All the sub-frames were vermilion with black wheels and axles.[4]

Once the Grand Canal Works came on stream all carriages were built there. New ones were needed quite soon and for a period Samuel Haughton oversaw their manufacture. There was much in the way of improvements. The later carriages no longer looked like road coaches: they were of the vertical-sided small-windowed type that had been the norm on most railways for many a year. New sub-frames which carried six wheels also became the norm.

The quality of the carriage work undertaken by the workmen of the

4   An example of one of these carriages can be seen in the Ulster Transport Museum.

Grand Canal is perhaps best exemplified by the state coach built there and which was used to bring Queen Victoria and Prince Albert from Kingstown to the city on the occasion of their visit in 1849. The queen was much impressed by it and commented on the beauty of its interior and its livery.

CHAPTER 6

ATMOSPHERIC TO DALKEY

A World First

In March 1844 the Dublin newspapers carried a notice to this effect:

ATMOSPHERIC RAILWAY
KINGSTOWN AND DALKEY

This railway will be opened for public traffic on
Friday next 29th inst.

The trains will start from Kingstown every hour and every half-hour from
eight am and from Dalkey every quarter and three-quarters of an hour from a
quarter-past eight am, till a quarter–past six pm.

Fares:

Second class carriage......threepence

Third class carriage......twopence

As yet there are not any first class coaches

By order
T.F. Bergin

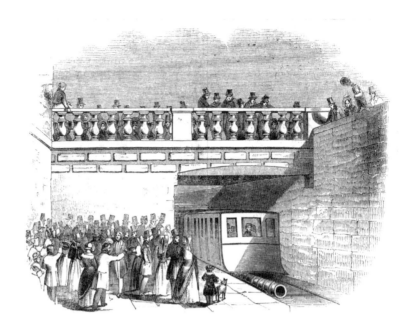

Fig. 6.1: *An atmospheric train leaving Kingstown Station (branch platform).*

There was now a train service from Kingstown onwards to Dalkey: this was to be the world's first commercial atmospheric railway system. The no locomotive train would be propelled by the effect of atmospheric pressure acting on a piston connected to the carriages, which ran on rails. The piston moved within a tube or pipe extending from Kingstown to Dalkey, the section of pipe ahead of the carriages being evacuated by a stationary pumping engine.

Before we go any further it is necessary to give some details both about the technology and about the path taken to Dalkey.

Pneumatic Transport: The Technology

It was the German scientist Otto von Guericke (1606-86) whose experiments first showed that useful mechanical work could be gained from the effect of a vacuum on a piston. There is a well-known woodcut (see Fig. 6.2: the 'Magdeburg experiment'), which depicts eight horses on the right and eight on the left trying to pull apart two evacuated hemispheres of

0.37 m diameter. Von Guericke calculated that a force of almost 10.9 kN was needed to accomplish this. In 1654 another experiment undertaken at Regensberg proved that a number of men were capable of pulling an airtight piston only about half-way up a cylindrical copper vessel. Von Guericke then attached his evacuated receiver to the space below the piston and succeeded in drawing the piston back down again against the force of the men pulling it up.

To von Guericke, therefore, must go the praise for discovering the underlying physical laws governing atmospheric propulsion. But to harness science we need engineering and the use of technologies. A number of names are associated with the beginnings of pneumatic transportation, in particular George Medhurst (1759-1827), John Vallance and R. Pinkus.

It was Medhurst who first evinced the idea that people and/ or goods could be transported by means of the reaction of atmospheric pressure against a vacuum. He published his ideas in a number of pamphlets[1] that contained a range of important statements. His first idea

---

1   G. Medhurst, 'New method of conveying letters and goods with great certainty and rapidity by air', London, 1810; 'Calculations and remarks tending to prove the practicability…of a plan for the rapid conveyance of goods and passengers upon an iron road through a tube of 30 feet in area, by the power and velocity of air', London, 1812; 'A new system of inland conveyance for goods and passengers…with the velocity of sixty miles an hour…without the aid of horses or any animal power', London, 1827.

Fig. 6.2: *The 'Magdeburg experiment'.*

was to fit a passenger-carrying carriage in a large tube which would have compressed air applied, thereby driving the carriage forward. However he was concerned that passengers might not take kindly to being transported within tubes, in the dark and exposed to compressed air, so he sought to develop a means by which passengers could be moved outside the tube, but by some form of pneumatic propulsion.

In his 1827 pamphlet Medhurst proposed three options for pneumatic railways: (a) a tube 24 inches in diameter laid below railway tracks; (b) a road carriage running over a 2-foot square cast-iron tube; (c) a goods track running inside a tube, attached to a passenger carriage running outside the tube.

Medhurst would never live to see his inventions become reality: he died in September 1827 and was buried in Shoreham on the south coast of England, the place of his birth.

John Vallance of Brighton took out a patent based on ideas similar to those contained in Medhurst's 1812 pamphlet, although how much he knew of Medhurst's work is unclear. Vallance built a prototype in his home in Brighton. The system had a tube 150 feet long and 8 feet in diameter, with a pair of rails set inside the tube within which a capsule ran. The capsule, carrying twenty passengers, was propelled through the tube at a speed of 2 mph. Unfortunately retardation of the capsule occurred due to the accidental opening of the door in the passenger compartment, making for an unpleasant experience for passengers. The system was lampooned as 'Vallance's suffocation scheme'.

Vallance founded a company (the London, Brighton and Shoreham Pneumatic Conveyance Company) to build his system, primarily for the transport of coal and bulky products. He failed to gain sufficient financial backing or patronage and by 1828 his plans had been abandoned.

Henry Pinkus is often named as one of the forefathers of pneumatic transportation but there is little basis for this assertion. He wrote to the editors of *The Civil Engineer and Architect's Journal* in Sept 1840, haughtily

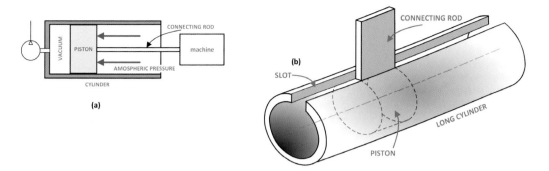

Figs. 6.3(a) and (b): The principle of atmospheric propulsion.

castigating them for attributing the discovery of pneumatic travel to Medhurst and claiming that he alone deserved this accolade. In their issue of November that same year the editors quite properly put him gently but firmly in his place by quoting from Medhurst's writings. They raised a number of points made by Medhurst that proved them right in their assertion. These points may also serve to explain the system and its problems.

Perhaps here a minor digression may help the reader. If we are to have utility from a piston in a cylinder which is evacuated, the piston being under the force of atmospheric pressure, whichever machine is to be operated by the movement of the piston must be connected to it. This is a simple matter if the range of motion is small. It simply needs a connecting rod (Fig. 6.3a). However if we wish the distance through which the piston is to move within the cylinder to be extended (several kilometres long, for example) the engineering solution is anything but simple, requiring a continuous slot (Fig. 6.3b). The slot must be sealed in a way that permits the connecting rod and piston to proceed along the tube. This problem was what plagued Vallance and Pinkus.

To return to the riposte of the *Journal* to Pinkus, the first extract the editors quoted was from Medhurst's pamphlet of 1812, page 16:

It is practical, upon the same principle to form a tube so as to leave a continuous communication between the inside and the outside of it, without suffering any part of the impelling air to escape; and, by this means to impel a carriage along an iron road, in the open air…' And later: '…the air must be forced into the tube behind it; but when it is to the contrary way, the same engine is to draw the air out of the tube before the carriage, that the atmospheric air may press into the tube behind the carriage and drive it in the contrary way.

Here we see clearly stated the concept of the atmospheric train. The editors also quoted from page 20 of the same pamphlet: 'A plan to combine the two modes together, that, the goods may be conveyed within the canal (tube), and communication made from the inside to the outside of it, so that a carriage may be impelled in the open air, to convey the passengers, would be an improvement desirable and practical…'

Although Medhurst went on to lament his lack of ingenuity in finding a practical means of sealing the slot in the tube, he clearly defined, in both words and diagrams, how it must work in order to be effective. Finally he wrote: 'Although the perfection of this work is not to be obtained but by time, skill, experience, and the wealth of a nation, yet, upon a smaller scale, and less rapidity, the expense will be more moderate, and within reach; and the value of it, compared with the present mode of transport, would be abundantly advantageous and desirable.'

Who knows what Medhurst might have done had he lived longer but it was left to others to develop a practical solution. These others did indeed come along, in the shape of Samuel Clegg[2], and the brothers Jacob and Joseph Samuda, who had an engineering and shipbuilding works on the Isle of Dogs in London. They were aware of the efforts of Medhurst

---

2   Samuel Clegg (1781-1861) was apprenticed to Boulton and Watt and at the Soho Manufactory witnessed many of William Murdoch's earlier experiments in the use of coal gas. Clegg invented the lime purifier. In 1815 and again in 1818 he patented a water meter, the basis of the current gas meter.

and Vallance and also of the shortcomings in their work and became interested in the possibilities of atmospheric railways.

On 3 January 1839 Clegg and Jacob Samuda filed for a patent 'for a new improvement in valves and the combination of them with machinery'. The lengthy patent document included the following statements:

These valves work on a hinge of leather or other flexible material which is practically airtight…The extremity of these valves is caused to fall into a trough containing a composition of bees wax and tallow or bees wax and oil or any substance which is solid at the temperature of the atmosphere, and becomes fluid when heated to a few degrees above it…When it is requisite to open the valve it is done by lifting out of the tallow with or without the application of heat and before named process of sealing it, or rendering it airtight, is repeated every time it is closed. This combination of valves with machinery is made in the application of these valves to railways or other purposes by a line of exhausted pipes for the purpose of obtaining a direct tractive force to move weights either on the railway or otherwise. This we effect by laying down a continuous length of pipe containing a lateral slit or opening its whole length; a piston is made to travel in this pipe by exhausting or drawing out the air from the pipe on one side of the piston and allowing free access to the atmosphere on the other side of it; an arm from this piston passes through the lateral opening to attach to the carriages on the railway and draws them along with it. The whole of this lateral opening is covered by the valve already described and that part of it through which the arm passes is lifted to allow it to pass and also for the admission of air to the piston…

Fig. 6.4 is an adaptation of the original drawing which accompanied the patent application (patent 1922) and it is hoped that the legend will explain the function of the elements of the system.[3]

We can see that the connecting plate (D), referred to as a 'coulter' in the parlance of the day, had its section bent at an oblique angle at the place where it passed through the valve. This was so that in passing it raised the valve as little as possible. The 'continuous' vacuum tube (A) was in fact composed of 10-foot sections of 15-inch cast-iron tube which knuckled into one another with a gasket of flax and tallow to allow for some movement while retaining an airtight joint.

The piston plate (C-C) was 10 feet in length and pivoted at its centre where it attached to plate D: this permitted a certain amount of play and allowed the piston to float and take up any irregularities in the vacuum tube/pipe. The vacuum tube also had its bore coated with tallow. The piston was fitted with two leather washers to produce a close fit in the tube, the interior tallow coating of which assisted sealing and easy piston movement. Another element of the design that was peculiar to the Dalkey railway was the weather protection flap or valve (H) which was constructed of 10-foot long strips of iron plate hinged as shown: this valve was lifted by the roller (M) as it passed along.

The weather flap gave the leather vacuum valve some protection from rain and other contaminants and from the attention of rodents. It was effective as Barry Gibbons, Dalkey Resident Engineer, reported to a meeting of the Institute of Civil Engineers after twelve months' service, 'that up to that time no difficulty had been encountered in keeping the leather valve in good order'. The absence of this weather valve on the two later atmospheric railways, Clegg's London and Croydon and Brunel's South Devon was a contributory factor in their failure.

In March 1834 Henry Pinkus gained a patent for a 'valvular cord' as

3   J. d'A. Samuda, *A Treatise on the Adaptation of Atmospheric Pressure to the Purposes of Locomotion on Railways*, London: John Weale, 1844.

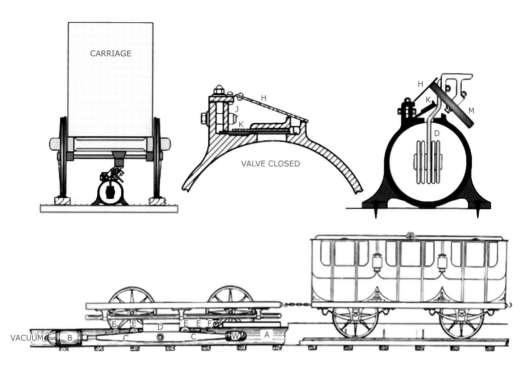

Fig. 6.4: *Drawing of valves and carriage in Samuda and Clegg's patent application.*

A *Continuous pipe fixed between the rails.*   B *Piston.*
C *Plate connected to the piston.*   D *Connecting plate to the piston and carriage.*
E *Metal rollers to open the continuous leather valve.*   F *Roller attached to carriage for closing valve.*
W *Counterweight to piston.*   H *Weather protection flap.*
M *Roller plate attached to carriage for opening the weather flap.* K *Continuous airtight hinged leather/iron flap valve.*
L *Composition for sealing valve.*

In the upper diagrams X-sections are given of how the carriage rides over the tube assembly, a detail of the elements of the flap valve system and of the piston and tube with the valve opened.

a method of sealing the slot on the tube of atmospheric lines. The method was no great advancement on Medhurst's self-confessed failures. In 1836 Pinkus sought and was granted a patent for 'improvements in inland transport'. In his application he described a valve made of iron segments affixed to felt and laid against pieces of wood which he proposed to fix in the trough surrounding the slot in the tube.

This methodology cannot have been a great success for in August 1839 Pinkus sought another patent for which he puts forward essentially

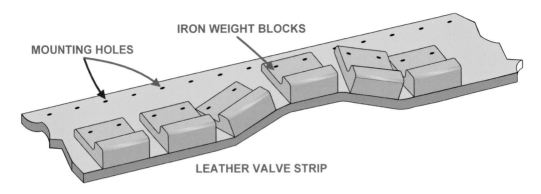

MOUNTING HOLES

IRON WEIGHT BLOCKS

LEATHER VALVE STRIP

Fig. 6.5: *Sketch of the leather strip valve.*

the same methods and materials used by Clegg and Samuda.

The editors of *The Civil Engineer and Architect's Journal* rightly laid all this before their readers, pointing out that Pinkus's last patent was registered eight months after Clegg and Samuda's and so they 'could not but think their invention was instrumental in leading Mr Pinkus to ideas of his proposed valve.' After this we hear no more of Pinkus.

The plan adopted by Clegg and Samuda was a leather flap seated over the slot. As the coupling came by, two small wheels running before it raised the flap and so gave passage. Behind the coupling the flap fell back over the slot and closed it. Theoretically, there should have been no leakage; in practice there was some. In 1838 Clegg demonstrated his system in Paris, again leaving plenty of time for Pinkus to pick up knowledge of its method and technologies. Incidentally the atmospheric system was subsequently used for the 1.8 km long Paris-St Germain line.

To summarise, we can establish that Vallance and Medhurst were responsible for the conceptual design of the atmospheric railway, Clegg and the Samudas for its embodiment design and Pinkus, who attempted no more than an embodiment of Medhurst's work, a failure. In this assertion I am supported by the writings of James Pim.[4]

4   Letters of James Pim, in *Irish Railway: The Atmospheric Railway*, London: J.L. Cox and Sons, 1841.

A flaw in the method of Samuda and Clegg's patent is the concept of a heater to 'reseal' the valve in against the slot after passage of the coulter. This shows a poor understanding of thermodynamics, the specific heat of materials and so on. They seem not to have thought of the speed of carriages along the track and the tiny amount of time the heater had at any one particular zone. The heater concept soon disappeared.

The technology of atmospheric railways went on to spawn a number of lines in Britain and mainland Europe. It lasted for some years, creating for a while a second railway mania with huge numbers of requests to parliament for permission for enabling bills. Gradually the thermodynamic and logistical inefficiencies of the system became more apparent as steam locomotives improved and also as the long-term stability and effectiveness of the sealing of the leather valve system became more and more of a problem. Very few systems remained in operation after 1880. However there is an interesting low-pressure air-propelled train system, the Airmovel, operating in Jakarta, Indonesia.[5]

The technology went on to be used in other ways and some of these uses persisted until the middle of the 20th century. Harking back to Medhurst's first ideas of transporting goods by air within a tube, the

---

5   For brevity I have ignored the significant contributions in this area of the American engineer Alfred Beach's pneumatic railways and the novel French atmospheric railway.

Fig. 6.6: Section of tube from Devon Railway showing the continuous slot. No tube from the Dalkey line was preserved.

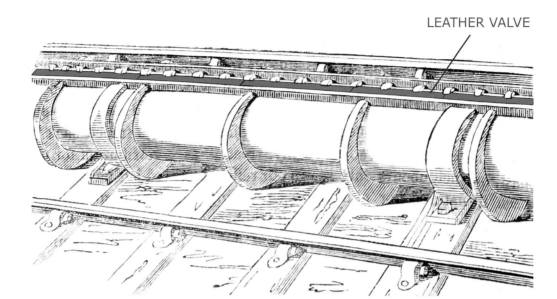

LEATHER VALVE

Fig. 6.7: Sketch of the tube showing the leather valve in place.

first pneumatic dispatch tubes began to appear. The British Post Office became interested in the system and a permanent line of 4-foot gauge was constructed between Euston railway station and the north-west district post office in Eversholt Street, a distance of approximately a third of a mile. Operation of the line started on 20 February 1863. A capsule conveying up to thirty-five bags of mail could make the short journey between terminals in one minute. Thirteen journeys were operated each day, with a daily operating cost of £1/4s/5d. The Post Office was charged a nominal fee for use of the service, presumably to encourage it to accept the technology. Other lines were created but the system failed because of the regularity with which the mail 'trucks' became stuck in the tunnels.

Those of us who are long-toothed enough can remember from decades past a wondrous device in large department stores such as Clery's and Pim's. The apparatus consisted of a network of evacuated tubes stretching from all the shop's counters to a central sales office. When a purchase was made our parents' money and a sales docket were fitted into a small torpedo which in turn was inserted via a special valve into one of

Fig. 6.8: First dispatch of mail bags to Euston. (Illustrated London News, *18 February 1863).*

the tubes of the machine and by magic whizzed away to the sales office. By equal magic (in fact atmospheric pressure propulsion) the docket and change were returned.

Credit is due to the D&KR for being courageous enough to espouse the newest technology and so create another world first with the atmospheric railway.

The Kingstown-Dalkey Tramway

The construction of Kingstown Harbour required vast amounts of stone. Richard Toutcher had purchased leases on Dalkey Quarries and philanthropically supplied the granite to build the piers, in order to see his life's ambition – Kingstown Harbour – completed.[6] To facilitate the moving of this mass of stone a tram or truckway was laid between Dalkey Quarries and Dunleary Harbour, the route of which was extended and altered as the construction of the piers went on.

The first section of tramway ran from Dalkey Quarries to what is now Queen's Road, east of the east pier. When it was decided to construct a second pier the tramway was extended towards the west. Spurs to access

6   Richard Toutcher (1758-1841) was later rewarded with a post as storekeeper/second engineer for the harbour. He remained in this post until his retirement in 1831.

Map 6.1: *The tramway from the east pier to Dalkey Quarry.*

Map 6.2: *The complete tramway, 1834 (in red).*

different parts of the harbour were laid as construction continued. Maps 6.1 and 6.2 give an idea of the extent of the tramway. I believe some parts of the track were in use by the harbour authorities until the 1880s but by the early twentieth century no tracks remained.

Parts of the original route of the track survive and have been turned into a dedicated pedestrian/cycle path through what is now a well-populated suburban area. The tramway was colloquially called 'the Metals' and the surviving sections of pathways are still popularly known by this name.

On 23 February 1843 parliament granted sanction to 'the perma-nent transfer of TRAMWAY, QUARRIES or other property, by the Commissioners of Public Works (acting as Commissioners of Kingstown Harbour), to the Directors of the Kingstown Railway Company, for the

Purpose of constructing a railway from Kingstown to Dalkey…'[7] With some modifications this tramway from the front of Kingstown Station to the Barnhill Road became the route of the Dalkey Atmospheric Railway.

DEVELOPMENT OF THE LINE

After the Dublin and Kingstown line was completed, the D&KR Company began to look further south. The next step would be to develop on to Dalkey: there although the population was low, the directors were sure a rail line would stimulate the construction of housing, bringing new customers, as it had done along the line to Kingstown.

When, in 1840, Clegg and Samuda demonstrated the atmospheric rail system in Wormwood Scrubs in London it worked quite well. It drew the attention of some of the foremost scientists and railway engineers of the day, notably William Cubitt, Charles Vignoles and I.K. Brunel, all of whom were engaged in the construction of new railway lines. It was also viewed by members of the D&KR company, including James Pim. Pim became an ardent supporter of the method and convinced his colleagues of its fitness for purpose on the Dalkey line.

Pim realised that he would need other powerful people to support and advance his views, so he wrote to the Earl of Ripon, President of the Board of Trade, to Lord Viscount Morpeth, Permanent Secretary for Ireland, and to others, careful letters explaining the functioning and extolling the inherent safety and economics of the atmospheric system. Pim also made much of the fact that an atmospheric railway in Ireland would be a distinct attraction to many. Behind some of Pim's attempts to convince influential people was the reality that money would again have to be borrowed from the Commissioners of Public Works.

The obvious path to Dalkey was along the tramway to the quarries, which was no longer needed as the harbour work was near completion. A deal was struck with the Kingstown Harbour Commissioners, the owners

---

7   *House of Commons Papers*: Paper No. 62, Vol. L, 197, 1843.

of the tramway, who gave over a half-width section to Dalkey.

Also Clegg and Samuda had offered the enticement of turning down royalties and had agreed to supply the necessary equipment to bring the railway into existence. The attractiveness of this proposition was obvious to the D&KR board and to convince the shareholders Bergin circulated a pamphlet in praise of the atmospheric railway.

By not seeking to raise funds through shares the D&KR avoided the complexity of seeking the sanction of an act of parliament. Once again they had decided to approach the Commissioners of Public Works for a loan and for permission to buy one half of the tramway to Dalkey Quarries from the Commissioners of Kingstown Harbour.[8]

The great seaward curve of the tramway between the harbour master's office and Kingstown Station made that section of it unusable for the continuance of the atmospheric line into the terminus (see Fig. 6.10). For the line to proceed to the terminus the D&KR had to get sanction for use of a section of harbour roadway between the two buildings.

Because of interruption to road traffic on this section of roadway an open cutting for the rail line was out of the question and so some over-cover was required. The question of how much was the cause of much argument. The Harbour Commissioners granted the D&KR a 999-year lease at a rent of £13 per acre on all parts of the roadway that remained uncovered. They also purchased for £285/15s a parcel of land near Dalkey which the D&KR rented for £20 per annum: here the company built its engine pumping house. With the agreement of the Commissioners and the sanction of the Lord Lieutenant a loan of £25,000 was advanced to the D&KR in September 1843. The Harbour Commissioners handed over the lands of the tramway on the 26 September 1843 and William Dargan was again contracted to complete the line.

However, one small matter remained: the Harbour Commissioners

8   In truth at this time the Commissioners of Public Works were also the Commissioners of Kingstown Harbour having, in 1831, been appointed as such by the Lord Lieutenant.

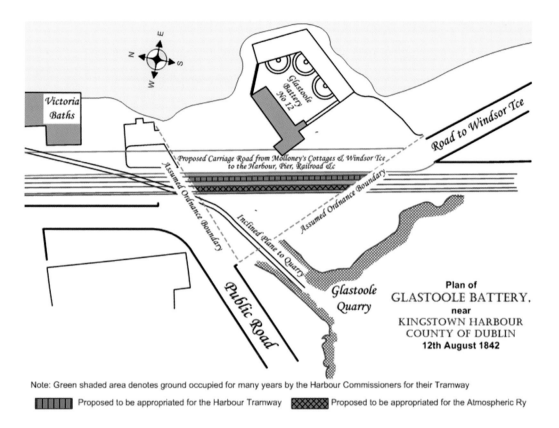

Note: Green shaded area denotes ground occupied for many years by the Harbour Commissioners for their Tramway

▮▮▮▮▮▮ Proposed to be appropriated for the Harbour Tramway   ✕✕✕✕✕ Proposed to be appropriated for the Atmospheric Ry

Fig. 6.9: The boundaries of the Board of Ordnance land at Battery No 12, Glastoole.

had for a number of years been using a small portion of ground where the tramway crossed the boundaries of Glastoole (sic) Battery No 12 without any legal right (see the olive-shaded portion of Fig. 6.9). Through the Board of Works the Commissioners requested the Board of Ordnance to make over this land to them. The Ordnance had no great objection to this as the battery was of limited use because the east pier blocked part of its line of fire. They agreed to give up the land provided a new battery was built at the end of the east pier. This was agreed, so the Ordnance lands at Glastoole, the battery and its Martello tower were yielded up. The battery on the east pier was eventually constructed in 1860. The D&KR at last had the line of road that would take the atmospheric railway to Dalkey.

Before all this was put in place, news of what was going on reached the ears of Kingstown residents who, in November 1842, protested to the Lord Lieutenant that their right of access to the harbour would be hindered and their property devalued by an 'illegal' extension of the railway across the harbour frontage. In a memorial, signed by fifty memorialists, the 'prayer' of the petition was that all work on the railway cease. The objectors did not have a substantial case as the Harbour Commissioners ruled that the public had no right of access to the harbour and in a letter of 2 February 1843 the Lord Lieutenant rejected their plea. His letter advised them: 'that if proceedings which have been taken and works which are now in progress, are illegal and injurious to you, if your view of the law be correct to take proceedings either at law, or in equity'. The protesters settled for requesting that the rail line should be in a tunnel.

The Lords of the Admiralty and the Treasury became embroiled in the affair and even the old matter of the compensation harbour was raised. The Commissioners of Public Works again asserted (using George III, Cap. 1919) that the Lord Lieutenant had sole jurisdiction over Kingstown Harbour. Much acrimonious correspondence passed between the parties, at the end of which the Admiralty and Treasury Lords backed down, but not before insisting that the railway should run enclosed in a tunnel to the outer edge of the east pier.

The memorialists were happy with this stipulation but the D&KR protested that the return by gravity to Kingstown could not work with a tunnel of this length. This was because the carriage occupied so much of the tunnel that wind resistance and the 1 in 228 incline at Kingstown Station would lower the momentum of the train so much as to cause it to halt before reaching the terminus. The Lords of the Treasury then stated that 'the railway company ought to cover in, without delay, the whole of the railway between the harbour-master's office and the terminus at the Forty Foot Road, with the exceptions only of such openings as might be required for light and air, and the Commissioners of Public Works be directed to enforce this.'

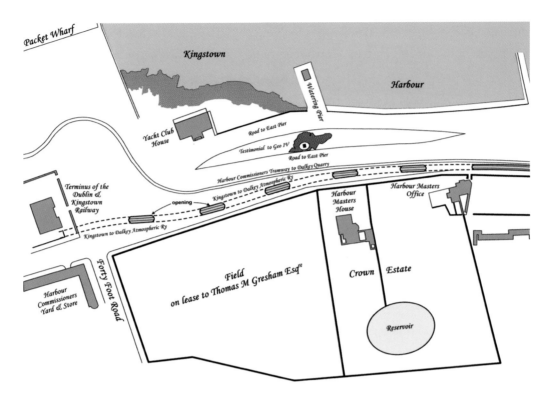

Fig. 6.10: J. Walker's preferred layout for the atmospheric line.

Eventually agreement was reached that the Lords of the Treasury should appoint J. Walker, a skilled engineer, to review the work on the railway. The D&KR agreed to pay all Walker's expenses and to abide by his findings. On 26 December 1843 Walker was asked to go to Kingstown to undertake a survey and report his findings. By 16 January 1844 he had completed his work and sent his report to the Treasury. This clearly showed that he understood the engineering difficulties a long tunnel posed for the D&KR. He proposed a carriageway of 116 feet from the edge of the footpath at Kingstown Station and that the remaining distance be divided into five covered spaces of 100 feet each and the same number of open spaces of 50 feet (see Fig. 6.10). These open spaces were to be railed off (see Fig. 6.11) and protected by strong road posts to prevent carriages coming too near the openings. The Treasury sanctioned Walker's recommendations and ordered that the necessary work be carried out immediately.

The orders of the Treasury and Walker's findings and designs were accepted by the D&KR and work began without delay. The method employed was by 'cut-and-cover' of a deeper cutting and by 9 March 1844 James Pim could report to their Lordships that the work was half complete.[9] The covering between the openings was made from girders that supported large plates of cast iron, all of which was then covered with soil and gravel. Whether from fatigue or corrosion or both, some of the plates later collapsed, fortunately without causing fatalities. Not long afterwards when the cutting was widened to accept a double track all coverings were replaced by footbridges.

The tunnel, the cutting, overbridges, railings, road, ballasting and the rail laying was undertaken by William Dargan. Samuda and Clegg were contracted to lay the vacuum pipe, 'with suitable self-acting entry and exit pipe valves and a steam engine of 100 horsepower with air pumps, to be fixed at Dalkey'. They were also to supply an electric telegraph and 'all the necessary apparatus and contingences', for completing and handing over the line in perfect running order, all for the sum of £11,000. This work Samuda and Clegg did in a most efficient way.

The telegraph supplied was manufactured and supplied by Cooke and Wheatstone[10] and was, most probably, a simple one- or two-needle type. It transmitted signals from the engineman at the pumping house to Kingstown Station and gave the 'away' signal for the train when sufficient vacuum had been established. The signal transmission path was over zinc-coated galvanised iron wires. This was the first use of an electric telegraphing system in Ireland. Whishaw[11] states that it was in operation on the line in

---

9   All these matters are dealt with in the voluminous and complex range of letters contained in *House of Commons Papers* HC 62, Vol. 50 1843 and HC 265, Vol. 3, 1844.

10   W.F. Cooke and C.W. Wheatstone, The Electric Telegraph, British Patent No. 8345, 21 Jan 1840.

11   F. Whishaw, 'On means of extending the railway into every part of the United Kingdom', *Transactions of the Royal Society Articles*, Vol. 55, pp. 1843-4.

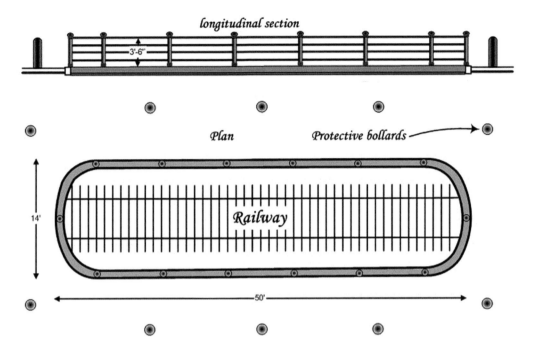

longitudinal section

Plan

Protective bollards

Railway

14'

3'-6"

50'

Fig. 6.11: *Walker's design for the openings in the over-cover.*

1844, Vignoles[12] says it eventually came into service, while Murray makes no mention of the system. I can find nothing further in the literature of its operation, its technical details or how the wires were strung between Kingstown and Dalkey. Before the telegraph operation was available the engineman carefully followed the timetable and established a vacuum one minute before the off for a train.

Now Kingstown station house had been built as a terminus and arriving Dublin trains ran into the railway sheds at the rear of the station so a line on the landward side of the station and a separate platform were constructed for new and ongoing passengers to Dalkey. The tunnel and cutting with its bridges had a clearance of only 8 feet 6 inches because there was no need to accommodate the chimneys of locomotives. The way had a short-falling gradient at Kingstown station (-1 in 228), to allow the

12 K.H. Vignoles, *Charles Blacker Vignoles: Romantic Engineer*, Cambridge: Cambridge University Press, 1982.

carriages, upon receipt of the away signal and release of the restraining brake, to leave the platform and roll down to the vacuum tube and for the piston assembly to insert itself the tube's entry valve. Once it was inserted in the tube the pressure of the atmosphere acting on the Kingstown face of the piston drove the train to Dalkey.

The line was 1¾ miles long and, apart from the short decline portion at Kingstown, rose by 71 feet in all, mostly at a gradient of 1 in 115, but with a 400 yard section of 1 in 57 at the Dalkey end. It included three curves in one ½ mile section; these varied from 570-700 foot radius.

Because the return journey from Dalkey was on a continuous downward gradient the trains could return by gravity, thus removing the need for atmospheric propulsion and a pumping engine for the Kingstown end. Gravity return was assisted by having the whole piston assembly held out of the vacuum tube, so that rolling friction, wind resistance and inertia were the only forces inhibiting motion.

The pump house was situated at the Dalkey end of the line. Little is known of it other than a (probably inaccurate) engraved image by Kirkwood (Fig. 6.12) and its location. An early OSI map shows it to have been located at the junction of what are now Barnhill Lawn and Atmospheric Road. The pumping house had adjacent condensation and boiler feed ponds (Map 6.3). The two storey-section housed the pumping engine and the single-storey part the boilers.

The station's location is given on the same OSI map (marked 'shed') some little distance from the Barnhill Road (see Map 6.3). No image or description of this building can be found and my belief is that it was, like the original Kingstown station, a humble wooden structure and so not considered worthy of either.

I presume that travellers, on leaving the station, walked along the tramway to Barnhill Road, thence to Dalkey.

When the line changed hands to the D&WR a new cutting was made, the track was relaid as shown and a new station in Dalkey proper was built. All the atmospheric track was removed, the stationary engine and vacuum tube were sold for scrap and all the buildings demolished. While the Metals survive only the smallest traces of the rest of the infrastructure can be found.[13] No one seems to have thought of preserving any of the vacuum tube or of creating a pictorial record for posterity.

All told, the extension from Kingstown to Dalkey had cost the D&KR about £39,000, which after ten years of mostly unprofitable service and the hand-over of the line was entirely lost to the company.

---

13 R. Goodbody, 'The Metals, from Dalkey to Dún Laoghaire', Dún Laoghaire Rathdown Council, 2010.

Map 6.3: *The locations of the track and buildings of the Dalkey Atmospheric Railway.*

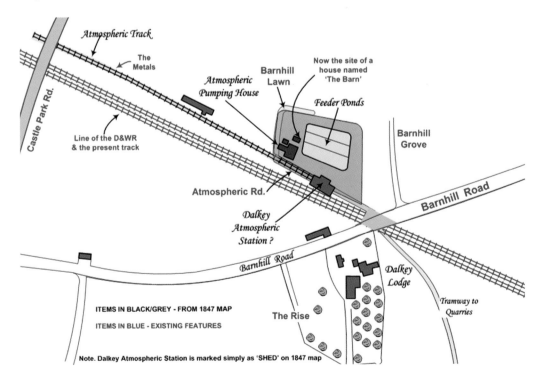

Fig. 6.12: The pumping house and ponds, looking towards Dublin, with Kingstown in the distance to the right.

THE PUMPING ENGINE AND HOUSE

Samuda and Clegg contracted William Fairbairn and Company to build the stationary steam engine for the Kingstown and Dalkey Atmospheric Railway. The directors of the D&KR decided that the maximum requirements for the line would be a load of 26 tons to be moved at a speed of 26 mph. An engine of 110 horsepower was ordered to meet this requirement. The engine was vertical and drove an overhead crankshaft with a huge flywheel of 36 feet in diameter. The vacuum pump was set above the cylinder and crankshaft and was 67 inches in diameter. It had an induction chamber at one side from which a duct led to a single induction valve at each end of the pump cylinder.

There was also a single outlet valve at each cylinder end, circular in shape and hinged like the induction valves. The engine cylinder was 34-34½ inches in diameter (according to various sources) with a 66-inch stroke working at 22½ strokes a minute under a pressure of 35 psi (although Murray claims 40 psi). Either of these values is very small for an engine of 100 horsepower. The pumping engine of the 50 horsepower engine of the London and Croydon had cylinders of 36 inches in diameter and a 72-inch stroke and operated at a higher steam pressure. At the time there were various methods for estimating the horsepower of an engine so it is more probable that it had a lower power than that quoted. Steam for the engine was supplied by Dublin-made Cornish boilers: three in number according to Murray; two according to both Clayton[14] and Grierson.

As the main vacuum tube stopped some 560 yards before reaching the station house/shed in Dalkey there was a lengthy exhaustion tube (440 metres) connecting the pump to the vacuum tube. The sections of the exhaustion tube were either badly designed or poorly manufactured. They gave trouble where they joined one another and a good deal of unnecessary leakage resulted. Many writers commented on the appearance of 'hoar frost' on the exhaustion and the vacuum pipes, which shows their failure to understand the endothermic (heat-absorbing) effects of changing the PVT (pressure, volume and temperature) state of a large body of air.

Barry Gibbons, engineer to the Dalkey and Kingstown Company, estimated that operating costs would have been 30 per cent lower if the engine and connecting tube had been better built.

Rails, Vacuum Tube and Rolling Stock

Again little information exists on the subject. The rails were said to be 'regular' and fixed in chairs mounted on continuous running longitudinal timbers. Vignoles stated: 'The Dalkey line was laid with "cast off" rails from the D&KR weighing 42 lbs per yard.'[15] Rails of this weight were much heavier than required, as without the presence of a locomotive engine a rail as light as 25 lbs per yard would have sufficed. Cross sleepers 9 feet by 9

---

14 Howard Clayton, *The Atmospheric Railways*. Lichfield: private publication, 1966.

15 'Minutes of the Proceedings of ICE' (Institute of Civil Engineers), Vol. 16, 1857, pp. 266-97.

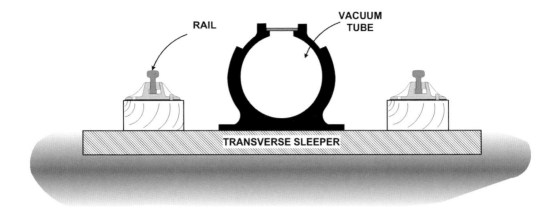

Fig. 6.13: *Cross-section of layout of Dalkey Atmospheric Railway.*

inches wide by 4½ inches deep supported the longitudinal timbers and the vacuum pipe (see Fig. 6.10). The sleepers and rail laid on a standard ballast were boxed, as per the main line.

The vacuum tube was of cast iron, made in 10-foot lengths with three strengthening ribs that were wider at the bottom (see Fig. 6.10). A Dublin manufactory made the pipes to Samuda's specification and no secondary machining was undertaken apart from the cutting of the slot and valve seating. The pipes jointed together by means of a spigot and socket arrangement at each end. Sealing of the pipe joints was effected by means of a wax and oil mastic, caulked with a hemp gasket soaked in pitch. To ensure good running the as cast inner bore of the pipes had a coating of hot tallow applied and were then reamed (widened) with a wooden plug of the same diameter as the piston. A form of hoop-like mounting chair held the pipe sections to the transverse sleepers (see Fig. 6.13).

I can find no images or descriptions of the entry/exit valves on the vacuum pipe.

Much has been written about the leaky nature of the leather 'sealing' valve on the vacuum pipe. However, Barry Gibbons was able to give the following facts about the operation of the Dalkey pumping engine: 'It was calculated, by means of an indicator, that 78 horsepower was required to work the air pump with the engine making 22½ strokes a minute and cut off at ¼ of a stroke. In this way the gauge was raised by one inch of mercury in fifteen seconds.'

On the subject of leakage Gibbons noted: 'When the engine is stopped the mercury fell one inch in 41 seconds. Therefore as much air leaked in 15+41 seconds, as was pumped out in 15 seconds, which meant that $15/56$ of the horsepower or 21 horsepower was required to overcome leakage. As the piston advanced along the tube the area of the valve through which air could leak grew less and this horsepower dropped to 4.3.'

This is not a disastrous level of leakage.

The atmospheric line had spacious new carriages suitable for safe running through the cutting, some of them composites of second and third classes. The third-class sections were open from waist-level up and had neither doors nor side windows. They sound anything but safe but until 1853, when a small boy was killed by leaning out, no accidents occurred. There were also second-class-only carriages but never any first-class carriages on the line. All carriages had glazed windows in their end sections. The 'superior' carriages or sections had glass panes fitted in the interior partitions affording a through view, which – contrary to some purple prose used to describe the wondrous sights seen on a journey – cannot have been exciting as the line ran entirely in a cutting. However, the glazing would have made the carriages seem light and roomy to the passengers.

No remnant of these carriages or even images of them remains.

The piston carriage was a composite guard's van and third-class carriage and had a screw brake operated by the driver/guard who also had the ability to open a venting valve in the piston to slow the train or bring it to a halt. Before starting on the return from Dalkey by gravity the guard inserted a lever into a square socket in the floor of the brake van, which enabled him to swing the whole piston assembly to one side: the journey took place with the piston out of the way. On reaching Kingstown the guard swung the piston back into position preparatory to its insertion into

the vacuum tube for the next uphill journey by atmospheric pressure.

RUNNING THE LINE

Great crowds came to view the wondrous new train system and the line brought increased business for the mainline D&KR and good revenue for the extension, as travelling on the atmospheric became the must-do experience of the day. By March 1844 a regular service of thirty-five trains a day was operating. At busy times the service was half-hourly, otherwise at hourly intervals, and an average of 4500 passengers a week travelled on the atmospheric. All passengers agreed that the journey was singularly smooth and, in contrast with locomotive travel, the freedom from smuts, hot cinders and smoke made for a very pleasant experience.

As the excitement of novelty waned, traffic faded and in the early period an average of four passengers per train became the norm. Loads varied greatly with the seasons. In winter the piston carriage and a composite one would generally be sufficient, whereas in the summer holiday season nine carriages might be required. These multi-carriage trains could weigh anything up to 70 tons all in and could only just get up to Dalkey.

Before the telegraph system the method of operating the line seemed to be one of carefully following the timetable. Five minutes before the train was due to depart from Kingstown, the engine in Dalkey began pumping. Station workers then pushed the train until the piston entered the tube through the special valve provided and it was then held on the brakes. The guard released the brakes and the train moved smoothly and almost silently away. I say 'almost' silently because there are records of people hearing the hiss of air entering the tube up to a few hundred yards away.

Average train speeds of 30 mph were attained: naturally, speed increased as the train moved along the tube, shortening the length of leather valve before it and consequently diminishing the leakage and increasing the power applied to the piston. The piston left the vacuum tube some hundreds of yards before reaching the station in Dalkey, so the train travelled up the steep 1:57 final incline under its own momentum. The brake was normally sufficient to bring the train to a halt but there were a few occasions when braking failed to prevent the train running through the station and off the rails. There are no reports of personal injury from these occurrences.

There were a few exceptions to this moderate speed with speeds of up to 70 mph recorded and one remarkable exception.

A DUBIOUS TRINITY FIRST

One notable day Frank Elrington, a TCD student and son of the then Regius Professor of Divinity, was seated in the leading carriage of the Dalkey Atmospheric Railway. Unknown to anyone, the carriage had become uncoupled from the rest of the train while all was being made ready. The pumping engine started up and the carriage, along with the astonished Frank, relieved of the weight of the rest of the train, hurtled along the line in the record time of 75 seconds. The average speed was 84 mph, which made Frank Elrington the fastest man on earth for a good many years.

Apart from the extraordinary rapidity of this journey, the line achieved speeds that would have been impossible for the locomotive engines of the time. In a report to a select committee of parliament Barry Gibbons said that the line between Kingstown and Dalkey stations was 2050 yards long and rose 71 feet, while that from Salthill to Kingstown Station was 1350 yards long with a rise of 13 feet. Yet the best locomotive engine of the D&KR in 1845 could not make the run between Salthill and the terminus as quickly as an atmospheric train could go from Kingstown to Dalkey.

At the other extreme, when returning to Kingstown by gravity, if the wind was in a certain direction, Gibbons reported that the train would come to a halt in certain 'flatter' parts of the cutting. Similarly, some of the very heavy trains returning to Kingstown would meet the short incline into the station and, lacking sufficient momentum, would come to a halt short of the station itself. The third-class passengers would then detrain and help the station staff push the train home.

The Demise of Dalkey Atmospheric Railway

The almost boyish enthusiasm engendered in many individuals by this form of travel seems to have blinded even hard-headed business and scientific people to the inherent faults of atmospheric propulsion. Obvious flaws began to make themselves felt at the economic and infrastructural level. The shortness of the journey and relatively low passenger numbers (leading to lighter trains) partially masked these defects on the Kingstown-Dalkey line but they became very evident and ruinous of some of the steeper and more heavily used lines that followed the Dalkey. Cubitt's London and Croydon (1844), Brunel's South Devon (1849) and Mallet's Paris-St Germain (1847) went out of service in 1847, 1848 and 1860 respectively. The flaws of the system can be summarised as follows:

Waste of Power

The air-pumping apparatus of the time was very inefficient. The pumping engine and air pumps had to be large enough for the heavy trains of peak traffic but were very little cheaper to run during periods of light use. The boiler in Dalkey had to be fuelled and running during the timetable hours (burning a ton of coal in four hours), yet it was supplying steam for only 10-12 minutes each hour.

The leather valve which seemed to work reasonably well on the short and relatively lightly-used Dalkey line was a significant problem for other atmospheric lines. The use of a natural material such as ox hide is inadvisable in an open environment. Unless well soaked in oily substances the leather will absorb moisture from rain and ambient humidity. This, along with the insult of the connecting bar/coulter, slowly weakened the material and caused it to tear at highly stressed points. Under winter conditions the heavily moistened leather froze, with consequent failure of function. (Stories of Rattus rattus causing the demise of atmospheric lines by dining on the valve strip are fairy tales.)

ECONOMICS

Although the cost per train mile on the Dalkey line was low, estimated at 1s/3d as against 2s/4½d on the mainline D&KR, in the long term the population of the Dalkey area was insufficient to support the line.

It is believed that the line would have been economic had it been extended onwards to Bray.

LACK OF FLEXIBILITY

A failure either in the air pumps or in the stationary engine completely shut down the line until repairs could be effected.

Because of the single-line structure of the Dalkey extension, it was not possible to use a rescue train to remove passengers speedily or bring repair crews to a train in difficulties on the line. An up-train travelling under gravity halted on some of the more horizontal sections of the line because of lost momentum required manual force to move it. These issues with flexibility coupled with problems at the pumping house were to bring about the railway's demise. The boilers required replacement and the engine was poorly manufactured and unreliable. This resulted in many stoppages that lasted for hours or even days and a consequent loss of trust in the system on the part of passengers.

The worst breakdown was on 24 November 1848 when a portion of a broken flap valve in the air-pumping cylinder was struck by the piston. The pump cylinder fractured and the piston rod became badly damaged. As a full repair could not be effected in a short time, the D&KR decided to adapt a locomotive engine, *Princess*, to run on the line. Alterations to the engine included having both her tank and chimney lowered to travel through the tunnel in Kingstown and the placing of a protective canopy over the footplate to protect the enginemen. *Princess* entered service on 23 December and worked the Dalkey line until the following 5 February, when the repaired air pump came back into service. As it was the winter season, *Princess* easily coped with the light traffic, readily pulling four carriages. This showed that, with some modifications to the cutting, newer, heavier locomotive power could handle longer and weightier trains.

We must remember that a major element in Pim's argument in favour of the atmospheric system was that it was impossible for the locomotives of the time (1843) to cope with significant gradients; this because they relied on wheel/rail friction (both static and dynamic) for tractive effort. Because the atmospheric system had no such need, Pim argued that this system was the only way of servicing such lines.

By 1854 the Kingstown-Dalkey line was the last atmospheric railway in the British Isles. It was not economic but the D&KR kept it running as the company was already in negotiation with others to cooperate in an extended line, with the minimum of an extension to Bray and perhaps even further south.

Also in 1846 the Board of Trade through an act of parliament[16] had ruled that henceforth all Irish railways must be 'Irish gauge' of 5 feet 3 inches. Although the act was not retrospective any change the D&KR might make to run locomotives through to Dalkey or beyond would have meant the laying of a third rail or a complete track renewal to conform to Irish gauge. This trapped the D&KR but in any case the atmospheric train service on the Dalkey line came to an end on 12 April 1854.

16 The Gauge of Irish Railways Act, Victoria Cap. 56 and 57, August 1846.

CHAPTER 7

LATER YEARS

The End of the D&KR

The foregoing is an attempt to describe the origins and early days of the D&KR; of course the line continued in existence and is still an active one today. In conclusion I will briefly note some events of the following years and their effects on the company and on its property, both mobile and stationary.

The period from 1834 to the late 1850s witnessed the approval and construction of many other railways in Ireland. The Dublin and Drogheda Railway (D&DR) received royal assent in August 1836 (6 and 7, William, Cap. 132). The track, under pressure from the Board of Trade, was built to the 5 feet 3 inches gauge standard, pre-empting the gauge act by some two years. The line opened on 25 May 1844 with trains running between temporary termini in Drogheda and the Royal Canal in Dublin. These temporary stations were soon replaced by Drogheda Station and the splendid Amiens Street station house. With the acquisition of the Ulster Railway in 1845 Dublin was connected to Belfast.

To serve the west of Ireland the Midland Great Western Railway (M&GWR) was granted royal assent in July 1845 (21-4, Victoria, Cap. 83) and was again built to a gauge width of 5 feet 3 inches. It ran from the present station site near Eyre Square in Galway to the splendid Broadstone Station in Dublin. As the century progressed the rail network in Connacht

was expanded, making Galway an important railhead, with connections to
Athenry, Ennis, Limerick and Sligo.

The south and south-west was served by the Great Southern and
Western Railway (GS&WR), which was incorporated in 1845 (7 and 8
Victoria, Cap. 100, 1844). The GS&WR grew, mainly by acquisitions, to
become the largest railway in Ireland, serving all counties below a line
drawn from Dublin through Athlone to Galway and also providing service
to the town of Sligo.

All these railways were conceived or constructed during the railway
mania period but, with the declining financial position of Ireland and the
onset of the terrible years of the Great Famine from 1845, capital from
investors was hard to find. Prime Minister Robert Peel was, however,
eager to promote the construction of railways in Ireland to provide jobs
for labouring men that would relieve the suffering of the Irish poor and
also help calm the ever-increasing bitterness and hatred between Catholic
tenant farmers and Protestant landowners. Accordingly he encouraged the
GS&WR to make changes for a route to Carlow with continuation to
Cashel in County Tipperary. This county was deemed the 'slaughterhouse
county' by the *Freeman's Journal* because of the level of death not only from
famine and its attendant diseases but because of the violence wrought on
landlords' agents.

Peel was a major shareholder (£900,000) in the London and Birmingham Railway, which in 1846 merged with others to become the
London and North-western Railway (L&NWR). He was therefore in a
powerful position to encourage L&NWR shareholders to grant significant financial support to the GS&WR. This suited the L&NWR as it had
its sights set on the lucrative steam packet and mails trade from Holyhead
to Dublin. (This commerce is why we find an L&NWR booking office
shown on the floor plan of Westland Row station, Fig. 7.2.)

Other eyes were looking at shipping routes between Ireland and
Britain. In autumn 1843 and again in autumn 1844 the Great Western

railwaymen, Isambard Kingdom Brunel and Daniel Gooch, quietly came to Ireland to spy out a route between Waterford and Dublin. Brunel had plans to extend a GWR line to Wales and develop a lucrative sea route between Fishguard and a townland called Walsheslough on the Wexford coast that we now call Rosslare. Communication with the capital would be essential so they determined to build a line through Waterford, Wexford and Wicklow to Dublin. The line between Waterford and Rosslare was eventually built (1906) by the Fishguard Rosslare Railways and Harbours Company, a joint venture between the GS&WR and the GWR. However for the line to Dublin the GWR had to decide how to come to terms with the D&KR.

When the Dalkey atmospheric line was up and running the businessmen of the D&KR looked to Bray: indeed at the same time as the Kingstown extension there were thoughts of this destination. James Pim was tasked to probe the matter quietly but little of substance occurred.

Around this time Brunel proposed that the GWR build a line through Waterford, Wexford and Wicklow and sought the support of the board of D&KR for his proposal. The D&KR felt it should make the Kingstown to Wicklow length and join the proposed GWR railway there but his did not at all suit the GWR, which lodged its own plans for Kingstown to Wicklow and Wexford. This bill was rejected.

Then, out of the blue, the GWR suggested they would build a railway, the Waterford, Wexford, Wicklow and Dublin Railway (3Ws) which would deviate inland at Shanganagh (near Shankill) and that the D&KR should build on to Shanganagh. This in turn prompted the D&KR board to consider they might be better to lease their line to the 3Ws railway and profit to the tune of £34,000 a year for little effort.[1]

Acts of parliament were passed in 1846 (9 and 10 Victoria, Cap. 208) to embody this and other railway proposals, including the formal

1   The figure of £34,000 plus 30 per cent of all revenue in excess of £55,000 was reached after much argument between Pim and Brunel and their respective boards.

incorporation of the 3Ws railway and sanction for the D&KR's extension from Dalkey to Bray. A most complicated set of arrangements relating to the phasing of the construction of railways, both long continuous routes and 'short', was brought into force.[2] It is enough for now to note that after a start in Bray the board of the 3Ws Railway ran into serious financial difficulties and had to pull in their horns.[3] In 1848 building of the line had stopped and the company changed its name from 3Ws to the Dublin and Wicklow Railway (D&WR). This was sanctioned by an act of parliament (14 and 15 Victoria, Cap. 108, 1851) which also allowed them to truncate the proposed line to run from Dublin to Wicklow.

There was at this time a plethora of other railway proposals and much complex dealing and plotting went on. William Dargan attempted to mediate: he bought up great amounts of D&WR stock held by the SWR and continued to do so, using bank loans to finance the purchases, until the D&WR was under Irish control. These huge stock holdings made him a very important person on the board of the D&WR and he eventually became its chairman. His presence on the D&WR board eased somewhat the dealings between it and the D&KR, although purchasing the holdings placed him in very difficult financial circumstances.

By 1854 two sections of line had already been built, a connection from Dublin to Bray (from a temporary terminus on Harcourt Road) and one from Shanganagh to Dalkey. It was now time for the D&KR board to accept the 1846 act and agree the lease of the Dublin and Kingstown Railway to the D&WR; this it did on 1 July 1856. The D&KR income from this arrangement had already been agreed (March 1846) by contract

---

2   H. Glynn, *A Reference Book to the Incorporated Railway Companies of Ireland.* London, J. Weale, 1847.

3   At this stage the 3Ws Railway company was riven by dissension and a section of the shareholders under Charles Nash were in rebellion against the board of the 3Ws, the GWR and its affiliate the South Wales Railway (SWR). This group alleged all manner of sharp practice by the 3Ws and GWR and continually appealed to the Railways Commissioners to intervene. See *House of Commons Papers* HC 71, Vol. 50, Sub-vol. 1, 1851.

Map 7.1: The Harcourt Street line (red) c. 1887.

at £34,000 per annum plus 30 per cent of surplus receipts. There was also an agreement for the D&WR to pay £5000 towards the new Kingstown station house. However, the original lease agreement had changed by 1856.

To quote Minhall Slaughter:

…Under clause 1-2 of the Act 9, Victoria, Cap. 213, the line is leased to the Dublin and Wicklow Company, at a rent of £34,000 per annum (and an additional or contingent rent of 30 percent of all the gross receipts on the Dublin and Kingstown proper, beyond £55,000 per annum) for 35 years from the date of release, and renewable for a second period…There was also a further 'Compensation or Diversion Rent', but by the Act 29 Victoria, Cap. 48, 1866, these several rents were commuted into one fixed yearly rent of £36,000 per annum, payable half-yearly, as from 1 January 1865. And 999 years were substituted for the thirty-five years of the original lease…[4]

4.   M. Slaughter (Secretary London Stock Exchange), 'Railway Intelligence 1869'.

All that remained was the alteration of the Dalkey Atmospheric Line for steam engines to run through. William Dargan undertook this work under the specifications and direction of Brunel, who was still the D&WR engineer. When it was completed the Board of Trade inspector rejected the line work as dangerous and many sections needed reengineering by Dargan to the specification of Barry Gibbons.

Dargan also built the Bray to Wicklow extension (the spoil from which was used to fill the inland section of Old Dunleary harbour cut off by the Kingstown extension). Through running to Wicklow began after the Lord Lieutenant officially opened the line on 29 October 1855.

From 1856 onwards the D&KR no longer ran a train service and was now a railway company in name only. In 1857 the D&KR section had its gauge altered to the Irish gauge (5 feet 3 inches), shortly after the D&WR took over. The lease and business arrangements between the two companies continued, but at times the relationship was a far from happy one.

After the conversion of the atmospheric line the absence of intermediate stations was remedied by the opening of small ticket offices in Glasthule/Sandycove and later on in Glenageary (21 August 1867). A section of the original line of the atmospheric in Glenageary was converted into a siding for the storage of wagons.

Something even a casual observer may note is that Westland Row Station is no longer a terminus. North-bound trains now issue above street level from its front. In 1865 the D&WR badly needed to modify the station to facilitate the rapid transfer of mails from trains to the Post Office vans. By this stage the original station was dingy and cramped, as passenger numbers had almost doubled since the 1830s. A portion of the cornice fell and killed a passenger in 1868 and on examination of the station's fabric a decision was made to undertake a substantial rebuild.

Through a bill in 1877 the D&WR obtained parliamentary powers to acquire the necessary lands compulsorily. Grierson relates: '…the lands were obtained, under a Government arbitrator's award, in the usual way, the many disreputable houses on the site were cleared away, decidedly improving the sanitary condition of that part of Dublin in which the terminus is situated.' Construction began and by 1884 the new station was nearly complete. The interior walls were of Dublin limestone in the lower parts and red brick above; the façade was of brick and ironwork.

The rebuilt station served for some time until it was decided that the line from Kingstown be joined with that of the Great Northern Railway track that terminated at Amiens Street Station; so an Act for the City of Dublin Junction Railway (CDJR) was moved in 1884. This was an expensive mile of rail track because of its elevated level. Completed in 1891, the Loopline ran on a series bridges over Westland Row, Great Brunswick Street, (now Pearse Street) and of course the Liffey Viaduct. Many of the road bridges were erected by A. Handyside and Company of Derby and London and the viaduct was designed by John Chaloner Smith, the engineer of the D&WR, with its ironwork supplied and erected by Arrol of Glasgow. The viaduct is a three-span bridge of wrought iron supported on pairs of cast iron cylindrical caissons sunk down to bedrock and concrete filled.

Fig. 7.1: The 1884 façade of Westland Row Station showing the openings for the Loopline connection.

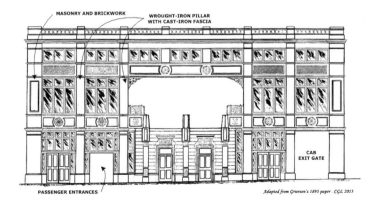

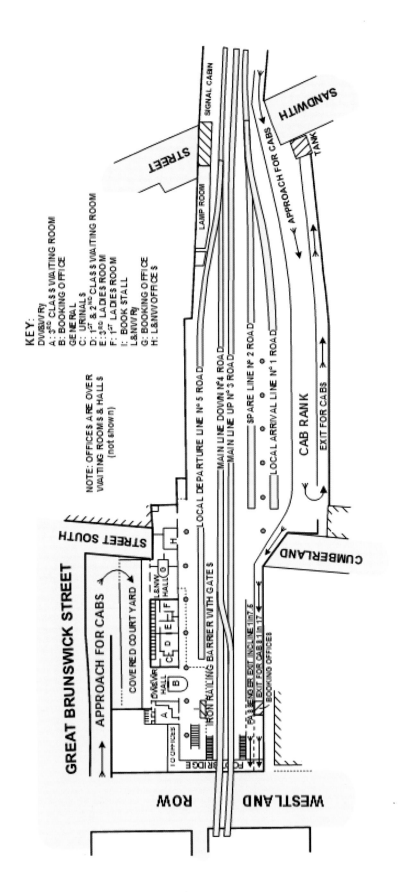

Fig. 7.2: General floor plan of Westland Row Station and railway lines, as of 1886.

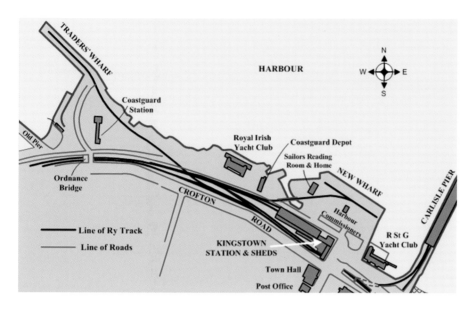

Fig. 7.3: *Details of the rail system in Kingstown Station c. 1907.*

Westland Row Station was readied for this continuation of rail by creating an opening in its frontage to allow two lines to run through. The new façade (Fig. 7.1) is typical of overly fussy Victorian design. The frontage between the two side walls is of wrought and cast-iron decorated by an orgy of cast-iron embellishments. (It does match the ironwork of the connecting bridge.)

The waiting rooms and lavatories were situated on the ground floor, as were the booking offices of the DW&WR and the London and North Western Railway (L&NWR)[5]. The secretary's and cashier's offices, the transfer offices and the boardroom were on the first floor. Access to these offices was via a footbridge at the Dublin end of the station (see Fig. 7.2).[6]

Apart from deterioration and an insult to its façade to cater for electrification of the line in 1981 the exterior of Westland Row Station has changed little since this time.

---

5. The L&NWR rented offices and waiting rooms to cater for passengers to and from the Kingstown steamships.

6. For full details of the station and its engineering see Grierson Part II.

Changes in Kingstown also took place, due to the opening in 1855 of the Traders' Wharf and the unfortunate choice of the New (Victoria) Wharf for the mail packets. The better to accommodate the mail packets it was decided to construct yet another pier within the harbour. This was called Carlisle Pier to honour G.W.F. Howard (1802-64), 7th Earl of Carlisle and twice Lord Lieutenant of Ireland. The pier opened on 23 Dec 1859. It had a single rail-track connection from the main line and a pair of tracks ran along the pier itself. Tracks were also laid from it to the Traders' Wharf and Victoria Wharf, in 1891 and 1863 respectively (see Figs. 6.12 and 6.13). In 1966 the lines to Victoria Wharf and the Traders' Wharf were removed and in 1981 with the electrification of the main track the line to Carlisle Pier was taken up.

An Act of 1860 (23 Victoria, Cap. 47) allowed the D&WR to change its name to the Dublin Wicklow and Wexford Railway (DW&WR). The company was not as financially successful as was hoped. The Wexford extension (1872) and the parlous state of some of Brunel's 'show off' engineering along the coast near Bray Head were partly to blame.

This shortfall in profit caused by the foregoing as well as other factors led to ongoing squabbling between the DW&WR and the board of D&KR over the cost of the lease. This was eventually reduced by an Act of 1906 which also permitted a change of name of the DW&WR to the Dublin and South-eastern Railway (DSER).

Squabbling continued until some much greater squabbles took precedence: the First World War, the Easter Rebellion of 1916 and the Civil War of 1922-3. The Irish Free State became a reality on 6 December 1922 and with the passage of the Republic of Ireland Act, the Republic of Ireland came into existence on 18 April 1949. These momentous events in Ireland's island history caused many changes and naturally affected all the country's transport links, both internal and external.

In 1944 with the passing of the Transport Act, bringing about the amalgamation of the DSER with the GWR and with the Dublin United

Fig. 7.4: *The mail-packet station on Carlisle Pier (c. 1908).*

Transport Company (trams and bus transport), a new company called Córas Iompair Éireann (CIÉ) was created. CIÉ was nationalised in 1945 and by 1958 all railways and most bus transport within the state came under its control. Many years later CIÉ divided and split its rail services between Iarnród Éireann and Dublin Area Rapid Transit (DART).

Two decades earlier the D&KR had staged its final scene. In 1924 the company agreed to a handsome buyout by the DSER, which gave good share-swap value to stockholders and generous severance fees to the officer board of the D&KR. Thereby the D&KR ceased to exist and so ends the story of Ireland's first rail company.

Lastly we may note that a railway which came into existence on the basis of the transport of freight from Kingstown to Dublin did almost nothing in this business, making all its profits from passengers and the mails. After a short time this failure to become a significant conveyor of freight did not greatly matter. The construction of the North Bull Wall on the north shore of Dublin Bay (1820-5) slowly modified conditions within the bay by changing the pattern of tidal scour over the sandbar; this along with repeated dredging of the river Liffey channel and deepening water over the sandbar revolutionised access to both to Dublin Bay and its port and allowed large ships to dock at newly-built quays.

We should marvel that a group of talented men in a little part of the then United Kingdom of Great Britain and Ireland had the foresight and courage to pioneer so many innovations.

BIBLIOGRAPHY

Barry, Michael. *Victorian Dublin Revealed.* Dublin: Andalus Press, 2011.

Bolton J., T. Carey, R. Goodbody and G. Clabby. *The Martello Towers of Dublin.* Dún Laoghaire Rathdown Council, 2012.

Boucher C. *John Rennie: The Life and Work of a Great Engineer.* Frome and London: Manchester University Press, 1963.

Clayton, Howard. *The Atmospheric Railways.* Lichfield: private publication, 1966.

Gooch, Daniel. *The Diaries of Sir Daniel Gooch, with an Introductory Notice by Sir Theodore Martin.* London: KCB, 1892.

Goodbody, R. 'The Metals from Dalkey to Dún Laoghaire.' Dún Laoghaire Rathdown Council, 2010.

Glynn H. *A Reference Book to the Incorporated Railways of Ireland.* London: John Weale, 1847.

Kohl J.G. *Travels in Ireland.* London, Bruce and Wyld, 1884.

McCann, G. *Ireland's Economic History.* London: Pluto Press, 2011.

Mulligan, F. *William Dargan 1799-1867*: *An Honourable Life*. Dublin: Lilliput Press, 2013.

Murray, K. *Ireland's First Railway*. Dublin: Irish Railway Record Society, 1981.

O'Brien, J. *Dear Dirty Dublin: A City in Distress, 1899-1916*. Berkeley and Los Angeles: University of California Press, 1982.

Pearson, P. *Between the Mountains and the Sea*. Dublin: O'Brien Press, 2007.

Pim, J. (Junior). *Irish Railway: The Atmospheric Railway*. London: J. L. Cox and Sons, 1841.

Rolt, L.T.C. *Isambard Kingdom Brunel*. London: Longmans, 1957.

Simmons, J. *The Railway in England and Wales, 1830-1914: The System and Its Working* (Volume 1). Leicester: Burns and Oates, 1978.

Slaughter, M. *Railway Intelligence, 1869*. London Stock Exchange, 1896.

Vignoles, K. H. *Charles Blacker Vignoles: Romantic Engineer*. Cambridge: Cambridge University Press, 1982.

Vignoles, O.J. *The Life of Charles Blacker Vignoles, Soldier and Civil Engineer: A Reminiscence of Early Railway History*. London: Longmans Greene and Company, 1889.

Thackeray, W.M. *The Irish Sketchbook and Contributions to the* Foreign Quarterly Review, 1842-4. London: Henry Frowde/OUP, 1863.

Whishaw, F. *Railways of Great Britain and Ireland, Practically Illustrated* (2nd edition). London: John Weale, 1842.

Williams F.S. *Our Iron Rails: their History, Construction and Influence*. London: Ingrams Cooke and Company, 1852.

OTHER SOURCES

Dublin Historical Record

    www.olddublinsociety.ie

Dublin Penny Journal

    https://archive.org/details/jstor_dublpennj

Walkers Hibernian Magazine

    http://catalog.hathitrust.org/Record/008696366

British Parliamentary Papers

    www.dippam.ac.uk/eppi

    www.parlipapers.chadwick.co.uk/home.do

Buildings and bridges

    archiseek.com

History of Blackrock Park

    www.ucd.ie/archeology/documentstore/hcreports/

Maps of Ireland, 19th and 20th century

    maps.osi.ie

UK parliamentary acts

    www.statutelaw.gov.uk

APPENDIX I

Description of the line of railroad from Dublin to Kingstown
(Adapted from Dublin Penny Journal *No 113, various dates, 1834)*

The entrance station is on the east side of Westland Row. The design is sufficiently characteristic of a public building without any attempt at embellishment.

The chief points worthy of attention are the beautiful granite door cases and cornices, from the rocks near Seapoint cliffs, and the light elegant iron roof over the passengers station. The details of the internal arrangements for the reception and distribution of passengers can only be explained by inspection, or by an examination of the plans and drawings; but it appears evident that the public accommodation has been studied in every respect. Indeed, nothing but system and simplicity could effect the arrival and departure of trains of carriages every quarter of an hour, without danger or confusion.

To preserve the ordinary traffic of the public thoroughfares, the railway starts at an elevation of about twenty feet from the surface and spans in succession over each street by flat elliptical arches. For the more important streets, smaller arches for the footways have been made on each side of the principal openings.

The intervals between the streets consist of high retaining walls of limestone, obtained from the Donnybrook quarries, the space between which has been filled with sand,

Fig. 1: Original frontage of
Westland Row Station.

Fig. 2: Train leaving Westland
Row (Jones, 1835).

gravel, dry rubbish and similar materials; the cartage gave employment, during the whole of the last autumn, winter and spring, to hundreds of the humble proprietors of carts and cars.

The breadth of the railway from Westland Row to Barrow Street, beyond the Grand Canal Docks, is nearly 60 feet [18.3 metres] between the parapets and is calculated to receive four lines of rails: the two central roads for the going and returning passenger trains, and the two exterior ones for the coal, granite, timber, and general merchandize-waggons [sic], which will load and unload with great facility at the sides, and without the slightest interruption to the continual stream of the passenger traffic.

The railway is carried across the quays, and a part of the Grand Canal docks, by a granite bridge of three oblique arches of peculiar workmanship, which, though well known in England, is now introduced for the first time in Ireland, and has drawn the attention and admiration of all the operative mechanics. One arch is intended for a future street, marked out, to pass parallel to the docks: a second is for the business of the quays; the third is to pass the boats of the trade and is provided with a towing-path, ranging with the general line of the dock wall. This bridge will form one of the most remarkable features of the works.

Some difficulties appear to have occurred in getting the railway past the distillery near the docks, at which it ought to be mentioned that a large station or depot is provided for the accommodation of trade. Over Barrow Street the arch is built with what is technically called kneed or elbow quoins; the stones being cut so as to form an oblique or skew bed on the face of the ring, and to return to a square bed within: these quoins are of granite – the rest of the archstones [sic] are of the usual limestone. At this place also the railroad contracts to a breadth of thirty feet, being adapted for two lines only for the remainder of the distance, the breadth between each of the lines of railway track being as much, however, as eight feet. The bridge over the Circular Road is square, but across the Irishtown Road the angle of intersection is only fifty-three degrees; and a granite elliptical arch,

built on the oblique principle, has been introduced with good effect. The intervals between the bridges are still sustained by retaining walls which, however, diminish in height, and the crossing at Haig's Distillery is the first accessible point to the railway from Dublin. This being but little frequented, the roadway has been raised by gentle approaches and passes on the level of the railroad. A neat lodge is built, and, according to the act of parliament, gates will be kept across the railway and a vigilant watch kept. We next come to a handsome bridge of three arches across the river Dodder, with a side opening for foot passengers. The railroad here approaches the surface of the country. A little further forward, and on the north side, are erecting the buildings for the repair and construction of the locomotive engines, coaches, waggons, & c. and the other necessary shops and conveniences for the company.

At Serpentine Avenue the railroad crosses on the present level of the road, with gates, lodge, & c. as before. All appearance of masonry now ceases: a green sod bank marks the boundary on each side, with a double row of quick-set plants on the top, which, in a few years, will form a fine hedge. Externally, the mound is formed like a light field fortification, with a berm or set-off, on which another hedgerow is planted. A very wide and deep trench forms an effectual fence against cattle and trespassers; and thus the line runs on through Simmonscourt fields, crossing Sandymount Lane and Sydney Parade, which will be protected, like the other roads, with gates, lodges, and watchmen. At Merrion the Strand Road is crossed close to the old baths, with similar protection, but on account of intrusion, the railway from Merrion Hall on to the strand is guarded by high stone fence-walls. From Old Merrion to the place where stood the bathing places at Blackrock, the railroad is elevated across the strand and at high water appears like a long mole stretching into the sea (See Plate I).

A smile will be raised at the recollection of the good-natured prediction of the direful and destructive effect the winter storms were to produce upon this attempt to force nature; and observing the facility and rapidity with which this embankment was completed, as well as that the effect of the storms has been to accumulate a

protecting bank at the footings of the outer slope, not the slightest apprehension can be entertained of any future danger from the severest eastwardly gales, when the stone facing next the sea is finished all along, as it has been completed in parts.

To afford additional stability and protection, an increased breadth is given to the banks seaward, which will form a delightful promenade on fine summer evenings. A cross embankment is made from opposite Booterstown Lane to the railway, to give an access to passengers; and it is the intention of the noble lord of the manor to cultivate the land thus redeemed by the railway operations, which will, therefore, in the course of a few months, present the appearance of a luxuriant garden, where lately was only a barren sandy beach. The quantity of land to be brought into use is about fifty English acres. At Williamstown, the railway nearly touches the shore by Seafort Parade and another access is afforded: while ample culverts allow the water to flow in as usual to the bathing places all along the coast, which, now that the construction of the sea embankment is nearly finished, will be as pure as ever, with the additional advantage of

Plate I: *From Blackrock looking towards Williamstown and Merrion.*

Plate II: *Lord Cloncurry's bridge and 'bathing temple'.*

being always smooth and still [see Plate I].

At Blackrock, the company are constructing bathing accommodation for both sexes, on the outer side of the railway embankment, to which approach will be had by a handsome footbridge from the high ground. These baths will be, as nearly as practicable, on their former sites. Access will also be had by a second cross embankment from the railway to Merrion Avenue, and handsome lodges, with waiting rooms for passengers, will be con-

structed at this station, as also at the cross bank from Booterstown.

From Blackrock to Kingstown the character of the work changes continually – high walling on the land side and open to the sea; then passing under Lord Cloncurry's demesne, between the beautiful granite pavilions erected for his lordship [*see* Plate II]; next, below the noble archway or tunnel; and beyond, through a deep, rocky excavation, upwards of 40 feet [12 metres] in depth [Plate III]; and below,

Plate III: *Lees's tunnel looking from the excavation towards Dublin.*

Plate IV: *From the footbridge at Seapoint Hotel looking towards Salthill.*

the bridge connecting the several portions of the elegant lawn of Sir Harcourt Lees; emerging from whence, the eye catches the noble sea-view, with the distant harbour. The road will now pass close under Seapoint boarding-house, [Plate III], which has been accommodated with a bridge over the railroad, descending to neat baths, and to a boat pier, and other conveniences. Again occurs a portion of deep cutting, through granite rocks, with a handsome bridge of granite, to the Martello tower at Seapoint, from whence to Salthill the railroad runs at the bottom of Monkstown cliffs, with an ample promenade on the sea side, and divided from the new foot-path by a neat iron railing [Plate IV].

All the rugged cliffs have been levelled down and formed into pleasing slopes, which the taste of the owner of the adjacent cottages will soon cover with flowers and shrubs.

The house at Salthill is now converting, with vast additions, into a splendid tavern,

Plate V: From the Martello tower (Ordnance) bridge at Seapoint looking towards Kingstown.

which will rival its celebrated namesake in the vicinity of Eton College, in all, it is to be hoped, except its extravagant charges; and the hill itself will be cut into beautiful terraces and slants, and planted in an ornamental manner. To this extent, terminating on the western pier of the old harbour of Dunleary, the works of the company are completed and nearly ready for opening; but the last portion, on which a commencement is now making, yet remains to be described. Four acts or scenes have been passed over, viz:

1st: the city, or mural portion, from Westland Row to Serpentine Avenue; 2nd: the country, or rural district, from that station to Old Merrion; 3rd: the isolated sea embankments, as far as Blackrock, and; 4th: the coast road portion under the cliffs, and among the rocks, with the boating and bathing accommodations seaward, as far as Salthill. What follows, though less beautiful, is not less useful, and may be styled the 5th, or commercial district. It commences by striking a chord line across a segment of the old harbour of Dunleary, which segment will be filled up, and, ere long, probably covered with bonded warehouses and yards. With the accommodation of an ample wharf, sufficient cranage, and other conveniences, the cargoes of colliers, steamers, and all trading vessels, may be quickly and economically transported to the railway wagons, and by these brought to Dublin at a very low rate.

The old harbour traversed, the railway will pass between the Martello Tower and the battery opposite Crofton Terrace. It will here be in deep cutting, and a granite bridge will preserve the communication with the old pier and landing place, with a considerable improvement in the approaches. Between the battery and the admiralty stores, the railroad will closely border on the harbour, and a convenient bonding-yard for timber may be formed with ready communication with the railway, whereby a great convenience would be afforded to the Canada and Baltic merchants. The road then goes at the back of the admiralty stores, and close to the boat harbour and landing place of the Royal harbour, and thence runs to a termination on the large open space opposite the Commissioners' yard and what is termed the Forty-Foot Road, being immediately connected with the magnificent quay and landing-place, now in course of construction by government, for the accommodation of the Post Office and other steamers; and when the works are completed, passengers may step from the railway coaches to the steamers, and again, on arriving will, with the mail bags, be conveyed from the Royal Harbour of George the Fourth to the centre of the Irish metropolis.

Stations will be erected at this end of the railway; and for the protection of the public, an iron railing will be placed between the railway and the common road, for the whole length of the harbour, from Dunleary to the Forty-Foot Road, and such communications will be made across as the harbour commissioners may direct.

In addition to the tavern at Salthill, a new hotel near Seapoint Martello tower, is spoken of. It is understood also that the company are about to erect splendid baths on a scale of accommodation hitherto unknown in this country; and in every point of view, the taste, the wants, and the wishes of the public will be studied and provided for; an excellent policy, which will be compensated by the additional intercourse of passengers upon the railway.

The preceding outline will convey to the distant reader, who may be familiar with the country between Dublin and Kingstown, some idea of the works, and of their general character; but to those who have not seen the beauties of Dublin Bay and its vicinity, it will be difficult to convey an adequate impression of the effect the railway will present.

Six locomotive engines have been built

Fig. 3: *The Sharp, Roberts locomotive* Hibernia.

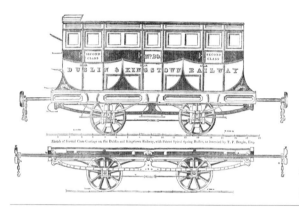

Fig. 4: *D&KR second-class carriage (DPJ 1835; illustrator E. Heyden).*

for the Dublin and Kingstown Railway: three of these are from the manufactory of Messrs. George Forrester and Co. of Liverpool; and three from the house of Messrs. Sharp, Roberts and Co. of Manchester.

The greatest mechanical perfection has been attained in these machines; and the useful and honorable rivalry between two such eminent houses, cannot but result in advantage to the present company as well as to the public, by combining superiority of workmanship with the most improved adaptation of principles.

A great and interesting experiment is also conducting at the same time, inasmuch as the 'working parts of the engines are totally different by each house. Messrs. Forrester have horizontal cylinders, fore and hind wheels of unequal diameter, elastic pistons working with improved valves, a small number of tubes in the boiler, & c. Messrs. Sharp, Roberts, and Co. have introduced vertical cylinders, the whole of the wheels alike, bell-crank motion, solid pistons, patent valves without friction; numerous tubes, & c. Both have put unequalled workmanship, both have adopted wrought iron frames, and straight axles, and, it is believed, have avoided all the errors and weaknesses observed in the locomotive engines hitherto produced.

The carriages for the accommodation of passengers are of three classes: most of these have been made in Dublin, by Mr Dawson of Capel Street; and by Messrs Courteney [sic] and Stephens of Blackhall Place. A few only were made in Manchester. The wheels, axles, & c. were necessarily constructed in England. Trucks are also provided for conveying gentlemen's carriages, & c. The railway coaches of the first and second class may be almost called elegant; the third class carriages are superior to those in use on the English railways, and all are covered. The fares will be on a very low scale.

It is impossible to describe all the details connected with the railway establishment, and indeed they would scarcely be interesting to the general reader. To form an accurate judgment, the work itself should be seen, and public curiosity and individual inquiry will be fully gratified.

The character of the works, the variety of the different constructions, and the costly expenditure upon the Dublin and Kingstown Railway, form a remarkable contrast to the appearance of flatness which the country presents to the eve of a casual observer, which, glancing over the level ground between the south side of Dublin and the shores of the bay, prompts the not unnatural remark, of the cheapness and facility with which a railway might have been constructed. But many causes have concurred in requiring a continual change in the transverse section of the railway, which have certainly greatly added to the novelty and interest of the work, though, at the same time, difficulties have been increased, and expenses augmented far beyond what has ever yet been required to force a level passage through the most difficult districts where railways have been introduced.

Among those causes may be enumerated the expediency of penetrating deeply into the centre of the metropolis; the attention requisite to be paid to public

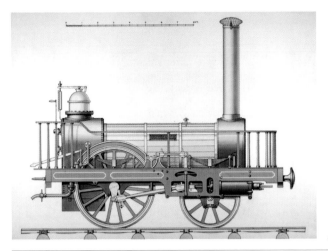

Fig. 5: The Forrester engine Vauxhall.

safety, and to vested and incorporated rights; the great value of the property, whether as building or suburban grounds; the interposition of secluded demesnes; the preservation of the bathing, boating, and other accommodations of individuals, and of the public along the coast; the necessity of making the course of the road as direct as possible, and of connecting the several changes of direction by easy curves, and the caution to be exercised in tracing a complete and isolated route, for the peculiar machines to be employed, through the rich and populous district in the vicinity of a large commercial city, to a termination on the quays of the finest artificial harbour in the world; where the smallest nautical convenience had to be preserved from interference, or to be amply compensated for and replaced; and close to the streets of a rising and populous borough, the conveniences and even the apprehensions of whose inhabitants had to be consulted.

On Saturday, the 4th instant, the first trial of the steam engine, *Vauxhall*, with a small train of carriages, filled with ladies and gentlemen, was made on the line of railway from Dublin to the Martello tower at Williamstown. The experiment is said to have given great satisfaction, not only as to the rapidity of motion, ease of conveyance, and facility of stopping, but the celerity with which the train passed, by means of the crossings, from one line of road to another. The distance was about two miles and a half, which was performed four times each way, at the rate of about 31 mph. The control over the machinery was complete, the stopping and reversing the motion was effected without a moment's delay.

On the 9th Dec. a train of carriages, crowded with ladies and gentlemen proceeded the entire length of the line, from the station-house at Westland Row to Salthill. There were eight carriages attached to the train; one of the first class, three second, and four of the third class.

The first trip was made by the locomotive engine, called the *Hibernia*; and with the many disadvantages attendant on a first starting, the trip, from the engine-house to Salt-hill, was performed in fifteen and a half minutes, and again back to Dublin in twenty-three minutes.

A second trip was made by the *Vauxhall* locomotive engine, which performed the journey to Kingstown in fourteen minutes and a half, and back to Dublin in twenty-two and a half minutes.

Notes to Appendix 1

The illustrations denominated 'Plate' are naïve and charming aquatints, although inaccurate – the work of Andrew Nicholl (1804-66). They were engraved by J. Harris.

Inferior and even more inaccurate black and-white versions of these appeared in *Dublin Penny Journal.*

(The *Dublin Penny Journal* was the 'red top' of its day and had a habit of embellishing the truth and creating fanciful images, in both words and pictures.)

Illustrations denominated 'Fig.' are insertions by the author and are from various sources, such as *Kirkwood's Railway Companion.*

Appendix II

Taken from The Repertory of Patent Inventions No XXI,

July 1836. Published by J.S. Hodson, London.

Specification of the Patent Granted to Thomas Fleming Bergin of Fair View Avenue in the City of Dublin, Gentleman, for improvements in Railway Carriages, which Improvements are applicable to other Purposes. Sealed, March 4 1835.

Within this document and after a lengthy preamble on the reasons for the introduction of his 'Buffing Apparatus' Bergin goes on to describe the device as, '….a combination of coiled springs, with rods proceeding from end to end of the carriage, designed not only to prevent the concussions at stopping or starting, but likewise any prejudicial effects taking place, in the event of two trains coming into contact; also to receive and transmit the motion of one carriage to another, free from that abruptness which is alike unpleasant to the passengers and detrimental to the vehicles.

Fig. 1(b) is a plan of the sub frame. A wrought-iron tube b-b, about three inches in diameter, the entire length of the carriage, and extending about two feet beyond each end, is supported on this frame by rollers, which allows the tube to be moved thereon lengthways with facility. On this tube is placed, at either end, within the frame of the carriage, about four feet of helical springs c-c, of graduated strengths; one end of each of these sets of springs abuts against a strong collar d, fixed to the tube b, and the other end against a small

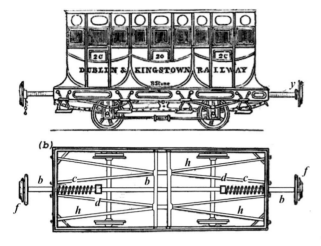

Fig. 1: Bergin's spring buffer.

box of iron attached to the frame, and furnished with one of the bearing rollers before-mentioned, also with two friction-rollers resting against the inner side of the carriage-frame end.

To each extremity of the tube b-b is attached a buffer-head f-f, by means of a rod of iron passing through the tube, and connected to the buffer-heads by screwed nuts sunken below their surfaces. At the back of each buffer-head is a cross-bar y, to which by chains and hooks, the carriages are attached together. This apparatus lies loosely on the axles, and is perfectly independent of the framework of the carriage, which is sustained by springs in the usual manner; and there are long vertical slots made in the framing, through which the buffing-tube passes, which permits the frame to rise or fall, according to the pressure of the load, without affecting the height of the buffing apparatus above the road.

The action is as follows: the train being moved in the direction of the arrows, the locomotive power is applied to the cross-bar y, and draws forward the central tube b, thereby compressing the springs c-c between the collar d and the friction roller-box f, which rests against the end of the carriage frame, without moving the latter until the elastic force of the compressed springs becomes sufficient to overcome the resistance presented by the friction of the carriage and load.

The carriage then begins to move forward so slowly, as almost to be imperceptible to persons seated within; the second and each succeeding carriage in the train is by similar means brought from a state of rest into motion. In case of one carriage running against another, the resistance is offered by the furthest end; the effect being to drive the tube b forward, compressing the springs at the opposite end from which the concussion is given; and the carriage will be but little affected by the blow, until the elasticity communicated to the springs, by compression, overpowers the resistance of the carriage, which then begins to move, actuated by a force just sufficient to start it.

The coiled springs are 4 feet in length, have a range of action of about 2 feet, beginning to be compressed by a force equal to about twenty pounds, and presenting a total resistance to entire compression of upwards of two tons. A spring of this strength, the patentee states, has been found suitable for carriages weighing, when loaded, about four tons.

It will be observed, that the entire resistance to the action of the springs is on the ends of the carriage frame; the middle of each is armed with a strong plate of iron, about 15 inches 2, through which pass the tension rods h-h to the outer angles of the opposite ends of the frame; consequently, these rods receive the entire force of the springs. The springs at either end of each carriage act totally independent of those at the other end, and of all the carriages in the train, except those to which they are attached; each has therefore to bear only its own share of the resistance of the entire train, the sum of which is made up of the separate resistances of all the springs acted upon…'

Appendix III

Extract from Parliamentary Papers, 1846

DUBLIN AND KINGSTOWN

1831 CAP. 69 SEPT 6

1834 CAP. 27 MAY 22

Principal Office: Westland Row, Dublin

Treasurer: James Pim Junior Esq.

Clerk of the Company: Thomas F. Bergin, Esq.

Engineer in Chief During Construction: Charles Vignoles, Esq.

Resident Engineer: B.D. Gibbons, Esq.

Directors

George Pim, Esq.,
Brennanstown Cabinteely (Chairman)

George Roe, Esq., Nutley
(Deputy Chairman)

Henry Roe, Esq., Fitzwilliam Square
Dublin

Thomas Pim, Esq., Monkstown

Joseph Kincaid, Esq., Leinster Street.

James Magee, Esq., Bagot Street

James Dawson, Esq., Kingstown

A.B. Kane, Esq., Kildare Street

Francis Low, Esq., Merrion Castle

Length 5 miles 60 chains. Stations at Booterstown, Blackrock, and Salthill. Terminates at Kingstown and at Dublin. With an extension to Dalkey, Atmospheric, total 6 miles 4 chains. Passes through the county of Dublin. Maximum gradient, 1 in 440; rise in feet per mile; 12. Royal Assent, 6th September 1831. Opened December 1834. Meetings, March, at Dublin. Cost per mile £59,122. Extended to Dalkey, 1½ miles, Atmospheric traction. Call, 50s. on half, 25s on quarter, Feb 25 1847.

Capital

2,000 Shares, £100 each; £100 paid. Whole shares
2,000 Shares £50 each; 2,000 shares, £25 each.

Authorised to be raised by shares	£200,000
Ditto by loan or mortgages	£152,000
Total sum to be expended to February 1845	£359,000

Cost of Working and Earnings

Total profits for the year ending August 1846	£10,043/13s[1]
Cost of working for the same period	£31,238/0s

Constitution

1846 Royal Assent, 16th July, extension to Bray and consolidate share into stock	£300,000

Completion, 5 years; Compulsion, 3 years

Extra Land, 20 acres; power to sell to Waterford, Wexford, Wicklow, and Dublin Company 1831: Additional Land, 10 acres; 1 Newspaper, Dublin

Quorum of meeting: 5 persons, 25 shares

---

1 We should note the still healthy but reduced profit when compared to 1839. (See Table 2.1, p. 34). This was due to other modes of transport becoming available on better roads.

Shares

1 to 5 have 1 vote. 5 additional have 1 vote additional.

Meetings, special, 20 persons and 50 shares.

£20 to be paid before transfer allowed.

Compulsory purchase, 3 years; Completion, 5 years.

Appendix IV

A copy of the flyleaf of the diary of Charles Blacker Vignoles for 1833

Charles Vignoles, Civil Engineer

Harrington Chambers,

St John St,

Liverpool.

No. 3 Westland Row, Dublin.

No. 4 Trafalgar Square, London.

Dublin & Kingstown Railway. Capital £200,000.

Traffic on the Rock Road out of Dublin for one year 1831-2[1]

Private Coaches	36,287	avge 2 persons each	72,574
Hackney Coaches	7,272	...4...	29,088
Private Cars	133,537	...4...	534,148
Public Cars	186,108	...4...	744,432
Gigs	24,175	...2...	48,350
Saddle Horses	46,164	...1...	92,328

1   Clearly journey numbers were based on 'out to' Kingstown and return. Vignoles's figures are a very good estimate, as can be seen when they are compared to the actual annual returns noted by Whishaw (See Table 2.1, p. 34).

Besides a vast number of persons on foot

	÷ Days 365	4,167
	In round numbers	4,000

4,000 at 6d = £100 per day =	£36,500 p.a.
Expenses and interest on loan say	£11,500 p.a.
	£25,000

= 5% on Capital of £500,000

INDEX

Act of Union 11, 12, 43, 44
Admiralty, Lords of the 106
A. Handyside and Company, Derby and London 127
Airmovel (Jakarta) 99
Albert, Prince 87
Alexander, William 27
Amiens Street Station 121, 127
Arrol, Glasgow 127
Atmospheric Road, Dalkey 110

Ballast Board 48
Barnhill Lawn, Dalkey 110
Barnhill Road, Dalkey 103, 110
Barrow Street 37, 137, 138
Barton, John 27
Bath Avenue (Irishtown Road) 38, 39, 138
Bellisle locomotive 83
Bergin's spring buffer 16, 85, 148-9
Bergin, Thomas Fleming 14, 16, 28, 31-2, 34, 80, 85, 89, 104, 148-9, 151
Bessler, Paul 65
Between the Mountains and the Sea (Pearson) 12
Blackrock 9, 13, 14, 16, 17, 19, 26, 28, 31, 32, 39, 42, 43, 44, 45, 46, 51, 58, 59, 61, 76, 78, 135, 139, 140, 142, 152
Blackrock Baths 14, 64-6
Blackrock House 26, 44, 45, 46
Blackrock Park 58
Blackrock Station 55-6, 57
Bligh, Captain William 19

Board of Ordnance 105
Board of Trade 103, 120, 121, 126
Booterstown 15, 16, 28, 35, 40, 41, 42, 56, 57, 58, 59, 60, 139, 140, 152
Booterstown Station 60
Bray, County Wicklow 36, 119, 120, 123, 124, 126, 130, 152
Britannia locomotive 81, 82
Broadstone Station 54, 121
Brunel, I.K. 72, 96, 103, 118, 123, 126, 130, 134
Burgoyne class (locomotive) 83
Burgoyne, Major General Sir John Fox 29, 42, 83
Butler, William Deane 54

Carlisle, Earl of 130
Carlisle Pier 15, 78, 130, 131
Castle Lyons 43
Catholic Emancipation 43
Cheltenham and Bromsgrove Railway 75
Chicken Rocks 21, 22
Circular (South Lotts) Road 37, 38, 138
City and County Borough of Dublin 58
City of Dublin Junction Railway (Loopline) 127
Civil Engineer and Architect's Journal 92, 98
Civil War (1922-3) 130
Clayton, Howard 113, 133

Clegg, Samuel 15, 94-6, 97, 98-9, 103, 104, 108, 112
Cloncurry, Baron (Lord) 16, 26, 42-5, 75, 140
Codling Rock 22
Coffey, Aeneas 63
Comet locomotive 80
Commissioners of Public Works 22, 23, 27, 29, 38, 42, 45, 48, 49, 51, 56, 83, 102-3, 104, 105, 106, 143
Cooke and Wheatstone 108
Córas Iompair Éireann (CIÉ) 131
Courtney and Stephens, Blackhall Place 63, 86, 145
Courtney Stephens and Bailey 76
Crofton Terrace 142
Cubitt, Sir William 15, 18, 19, 39, 48, 103, 118
Cyclops locomotive 83

Dalkey 1, 3, 5, 7, 9, 15, 16, 20, 23, 36, 49, 51, 123, 124, 126, 133, 152
Dalkey Atmospheric Railway 7, 15, 89-120
Dalkey Quarries 51, 101, 103
Dalkey Tramway 7, 101
Dargan, William 13, 30, 31, 42, 47, 51, 55, 64, 69, 70, 71, 104, 108, 124-6, 134
DART 17, 55, 62, 131
Dawson, James 151
Dawsons (Capel Street) 86, 145
de Grey, Earl 83

Dock Distillery 63
Dodder, River 32, 39, 138
Donnybrook 38, 136
Drogheda Station 121
Dublin and Drogheda Railway
    (D&DR) 121
Dublin and Kingstown Railway
    Company 26
Dublin and South-Eastern Railway
    (DSER) 63, 130
Dublin and Wicklow Railway
    (D&WR) 30, 110, 124, 125,
    126, 127, 130
Dublin Bay 19, 20, 131, 132, 143
Dublin Chamber of Commerce 26
Dublin-Dunleary ship canal 15,
    19, 23, 25, 26
Dublin Gas Works 82
Dublin Historical Record 19, 135
Dublin locomotive 79, 81
Dublin Penny Journal 6, 13, 28, 82,
    135, 136, 147
Dublin Port 18-20
Dublin United Transport Company
    (DUTC) 130
Dublin Wicklow and Wexford
    Railway (DW&WR) 61, 130
Dublin Wide Streets
    Commissioners 38
Dundrum 58
Dún Laoghaire (Dunleary) 9, 14,
    15, 18, 20, 21-3, 50, 54, 58,
    64, 76, 78, 101, 111, 133, 126,
    142, 143
Dunleary Coffee House 14, 54

Easter Rebellion (1916) 130
east pier, Dún Laoghaire 15, 16,
    22-3, 47, 54, 101, 102, 105, 106
electric telegraph 108
Elrington, Frank 117
Euston Station, London 15, 100,
    101

Fairbairn, William 39, 112
Ferrier, James 27
First World War 130
Fishguard 123

Fishguard Rosslare Railways and
    Harbours Company 123
Forrester locomotives 16, 79, 80,
    81, 82, 144, 146
Forty Foot 23, 36, 106
Forty-Foot Road 143
Freeman's Journal 122
freight transport on D&KR 83,
    131

Galloways of Glasgow 85
Galway 12, 54, 121, 122
Gamble, Norman 7
Gaslight system 78
George Forrester and Company 79
George IV 23, 143
Gibbons, Barry 39, 96, 113, 114-5,
    117, 126, 151
Glasthule (Glastoole) 15, 105, 126
Glenageary 126
Gooch, Daniel 123, 133
Grand Canal 10, 25, 26, 27, 36, 37,
    38, 40, 57, 62, 63, 71, 78, 83, 86,
    87, 137
Grand Canal Company 25, 26,
    27, 36
Grand Canal Dock 10, 37, 38,
    63, 71
Grand Canal Works 40, 62, 63,
    83, 86
Grand Orange Lodge of Ireland
    44
Great Brunswick Street 27, 28, 127
Great Famine 12, 122
Great Northern Railway 127
Great Southern and Western
    Railway (GS&WR) 122, 123
Great Western Railway (GWR)
    72, 73, 121, 122, 123, 124, 130
Gresham Hotel, Dublin 36
Gresham, Thomas 36
Grierson, Thomas 7, 37, 46, 47, 53,
    70, 113, 126, 129

Haig's Distillery 39, 61, 138
Haig's Lane 62
Harcourt Road 124
Harcourt Street railway line 16
Haughton, Samuel 30, 83, 86

Hibernia locomotive 16, 31, 33, 81,
    144, 147
Hibernian Gas Company 77
Holyhead 30, 31, 35, 42, 122
Home Rule 43
Horsley Iron Company, Yorkshire
    80
Howth Harbour 18, 20

Iarnród Éireann 131
Institute of Civil Engineers 96,
    113
Irish Free State 18, 130
Irish gauge 120, 121, 126
Irish Railway Record Society 13,
    134
Irish Sketchbook (Thackeray) 12, 134
Irishtown 38, 58, 138

John Bradley and Company 70
Jupiter locomotive 83

Kane, A. B. 151
Kincaid, Joseph 27, 151
Kingstown-Dalkey Tramway
    101-3, 104
Kingstown Harbour 17, 18, 23, 47,
    64, 104, 106
Kingstown Harbour
    Commissioners 22, 23,103-6
Kingstown locomotive 79
*Kirkwood's Dublin and Kingstown
    Railway Companion* 110, 147
kyanising process 72-3
Kyan, John Howard 72

Lansdowne Road 57, 62, 76
Lees, Sir Harcourt 13, 16, 26, 42,
    43-5, 47, 141
Liffey, River 19, 38, 127, 132
Liverpool and Holyhead steam
    packets 35
Liverpool and Manchester Railway
    (L&MR) 83
London and Birmingham Railway
    122
London and Croydon Atmospheric
    Railway 75, 96, 113, 118

London and Manchester Railway 80
London and North-western Railway (L&NWR) 122, 129
London, Brighton and Shoreham Pneumatic Conveyance Company 92
Longford, Earl of 31
Longford Gardens 64
Lord Lieutenant 23, 44, 49, 83, 104, 106, 126, 130
Low, Francis 151
Lyons estate 43

Magdeburg experiment 14, 90, 91
Magee, James 151
Mallet, J. & R. 63
Manchester locomotive 82
Maretimo 20, 26, 43, 45, 75
Maretimo House 20, 43
Marine Road, Dún Laoghaire 36
Martello towers 13, 14, 16, 47, 48, 49, 50, 76, 105, 133, 141, 142, 143, 146
Medhurst, George 91, 92-4, 97, 98, 99
Menai Bridge 30
Merrion 139
Merrion Avenue 140
Merrion Hall 139
Merrion Road 20, 82
Merrion Square 58
Merrion Station 62
Metals, the 9, 101-2, 111, 133
Midland Great Western Railway (M&GWR) 121
Monkstown 24, 141, 151
Mornington House 43
Morpeth, Lord Viscount 103
Mount Merrion 58
Mount Street 24
Mulgrave 49
Mulvany, J.S. 54, 55, 56
Murdoch, William 94
Murray, K.A. 7, 74, 109, 113, 134

Nash, Charles 124
National Railway Museum UK 7

New (Victoria) Wharf 35, 48, 50, 130
Nicholl, Andrew 33, 147
Nimmo, Alexander 26, 29
North Bull Wall 131

O'Connell, Daniel 36, 43
Old Dunleary Harbour 14, 21, 23, 28, 35, 47, 48, 51, 61
Old Dunleary Pier 21
Old Merrion 139, 142
Ordnance Battery 48
Ordnance Survey Ireland (OSI) 36, 46, 135

Page, Sir Thomas 19
Pandrol clip 8, 14, 75
Paris-St Germain Atmospheric Railway 98, 118
Pavilion Gardens, Dún Laoghaire 14
Peafield Baths 65
Peel, Sir Robert 122
Pembroke Commissioners 60
Pembroke, Earl of 56, 58
Pembroke estate 58, 61, 62
Pembroke township 58
Ringsend 19, 23
Peninsular War 20
Perrin, Serjeant 44
Perry, Captain John 19
Perry, James 27
Pim, George 151
Pim, James Junior 26, 27, 28, 29-30, 44, 45, 48, 82, 98, 103, 108, 120, 123, 151
Pim, Richard 30, 83
Pim, Thomas 27, 151
Pinkus, R. 91, 92, 93, 96, 97, 98
postal (mail) service 20, 23, 54, 84, 122, 126, 131
mail packet ships 20, 23
Prince of Wales 19, 20
Princess locomotive 7, 14, 82, 83, 119-20
Purty Kitchen 54

Quakers (Society of Friends) 25-6, 27, 36

'Quaker' engines 83
'Quakers' line' 25-6
Queen's Road, Dún Laoghaire 101

Railway Cottages 62
railway mania 122
railway mania (atmospheric) 99
Railways Commissioners 124
Regensberg (experiment) 91
Rennie, John, the elder 13, 20, 22, 23, 133
Republic of Ireland Act, 1949 130
Ringsend 19, 23, 58
Ripon, Earl of 103
Roberts, Samuel 54, 55
Rochdale 13, 19, 20
Rock Road 28, 57, 60, 154
Roe, George 151
Roe, Henry 151
Roe, Robert 27
Rolfson, Per Pande 75
Rosslare 123
Royal Canal 121
Royal Dublin Society (RDS) 30, 82
Royal Harbour of Kingstown 23, 24, 60, 143
Royal Hotel Kingstown 36
Royal Irish Academy 27, 30
Royal (Marine) Hotel, Dún Laoghaire 36
Royal Marine Road, Dún Laoghaire 36

Salthill 14, 16, 28, 31, 33, 35, 37, 47, 52, 57, 60, 61, 64, 65, 66, 71, 76, 78, 117, 141, 142, 143, 147, 152
Salthill Baths 65-6
Salthill Hotel 14, 33, 60, 64-5, 66, 78
Salthill Station 61
Samuda brothers (Jacob and Joseph) 15, 94-5, 98, 99, 103, 108, 112
Samuda, Jacob 95, 104, 108, 114
Sandycove 78, 126
Sandymount 37, 57, 59, 60, 62, 76, 139

Sandymount Lane 37, 57, 59, 60, 62, 76, 139
Saunders Newsletter 31
Scotsman's Bay 23
sea bathing 65, 146
Seafield Avenue 46
Seafort Parade 139
Seapoint 13, 16, 19, 20, 46, 47, 57, 61, 76, 136, 141, 142, 143
Seapoint Station 60-1
semaphore signals 77-8
Serpentine Avenue 13, 37, 39, 57, 59, 76, 82, 138, 142
Serpentine Road 62, 63
Shanganagh 123, 124
Sharp, Roberts and Company, Manchester 14, 16, 79, 80, 85, 144, 159
Simmonscourt gravel pit 38, 139
skew bridges 38, 39, 138
Slaughter, Minhall 125
Smith, John Chaloner 127
South Devon Atmospheric Railway 96, 118
South Lotts Road 37, 38, 39
South Wales Railway (SWR) 124
Stanley Sands, Holyhead 31, 42
Star locomotive 80, 82, 83
state coach, 1849 87
St Begnet's Dalkey 20
steam packets 35, 48
Stephenson, Robert 67
Stephenson's gauge 67
Stockton and Darlington Railway (S&DR) 25, 27, 67, 83
Strand Road 139

Sussex Parade 36
Sydney Gate 76
Sydney Parade 57, 60, 139

tank engines 81
telegraph system (Dalkey Atmospheric Railway) 116
Telford, Thomas 30, 42
Thackeray, W.M. 12, 77, 134
Thomas Clarendon's riding school 27
Toutcher, Captain Richard 21, 23, 101
Traders' Wharf 130
Transport Act, 1944 130
Travels in Ireland (Kohl) 12, 133
Treasury, Lords of the 27, 49, 106, 107, 108
Trinity College Dublin (TCD) 2, 7, 9, 10, 27, 28, 43, 117
Twigg, James 27

Ulster Railway 121
Ulster Transport Museum 8, 86

Vallance, John 91, 92, 93, 95, 98
Vallencey, General Charles 21
Vance's Harbour 46
Vauxhall Foundry, Liverpool 79
Vauxhall locomotive 16, 31, 32, 79, 146, 147
Victoria Baths 66
Victoria locomotive 80
Victorian Dublin Revealed (Barry) 12
Victoria, Queen 87

Victoria Wharf 36, 130
Vignoles, Charles Blacker 6, 13, 14, 29, 30, 38, 42, 47, 65, 67, 69, 71,-5, 103, 109, 113, 134, 151, 154
Vignoles-Stevens rail 73
von Guericke, Otto 90, 91
Vulcan locomotive 83

Walker, J. 15, 107, 108, 109
Walker's Hibernian Magazine 13
Waterford, Wexford, Wicklow and Dublin Railway (3Ws) 123-4
Wenlock, Debra 7, 14
Westland Row 13, 28, 31, 32, 33, 37, 40, 53, 58, 59, 60, 63, 75, 78, 122, 136, 137, 142, 147, 151
Westland Row Station 14, 15, 16, 33, 51-2, 126-9, 137
west pier, Dún Laoghaire 22, 28, 35, 47, 61, 66, 76, 78, 142
Wexford 123, 152
Whishaw, Frederick 33, 34, 70, 74, 84, 108, 134, 154
Whitworth, Earl 23
Wicklow 123, 152
William Fairbairn and Company 112
Williams, Frederick 68
Williamstown 16, 28, 31, 42, 56, 57, 59, 60, 139, 140, 146
Williamstown Station 60